Maths for the More Able – A Challenge a Week

YEAR 5

Dr Alan Stoker

Introduction

This series of six photocopiable books provides additional challenge for more able children. The materials enable you to meet the needs of able mathematicians without developing completely separate topics.

For users of the NNS
Maths For the More Able can be integrated easily into whatever maths material you use if you are following the NNS. The contents list on the inside front cover gives the appropriate reference to the NNS pages. The book contains stimulating challenges to enhance the range of children's mathematical experience.

You can use this book to:
- provide alternative, and more demanding, tasks for more able children during the group work phase of the daily maths lesson;
- provide more challenging homework tasks for the more able mathematicians in your class;
- broaden the range of mathematical experience for a range of children.

Many of the tasks in this book are of an investigative or puzzle-solving variety. In addition to mathematical knowledge, some logical thinking will often be required. The children should enjoy the level of challenge the activities provide, and

also the opportunity to choose their own ways of working. This is fundamental to development in mathematics, and you should therefore allow children to decide what aids they will use to help them solve the problems. More able children are often comfortable with abstract tasks, but most of them will at some stage want to use practical apparatus, and this should be allowed.

For users of the Folens Maths Programme
The teacher's pages are correlated to specific lessons in the FMP. You can therefore substitute for your able pupils the activity in this book for the one indicated for that day in the FMP.

The pupil sheets
Photocopiable activity sheets (**AS**) for the children to work on are provided for the lessons and can be used to support group work. It is assumed that all the children will take part in the whole-class introduction to the lesson before tackling the task from this book. Note that Week 7 in each term is set aside for assessment and review.

The teacher notes will guide you in introducing the tasks to the children and in effective ways of working, as well as providing the solutions. These notes will help you to support children appropriately as they work.

Place value, ordering and rounding

Learning objectives

◆ Sort numbers and put them in ascending and descending order.
◆ Read and write numbers with up to seven digits.

Resources

AS 'Rearrange the digits'

Teacher's notes

In this activity the digits in a number are rearranged to make new numbers. The aim is to make a new number that is as close as possible to that specified.

In the example, the digits 1, 2, 3 are rearranged to make a new number that is about 100 greater than 123. The closest that can be achieved is 231. Ensure that the pupils understand the example. Ask them to carry out the necessary calculations without using a calculator.

1. The first number has four digits: 3579.
The aim is to rearrange the digits 3, 5, 7, 9 to make a number that is about 2000 greater than 3579.
Start with the first digit; this will probably be 5.
Then move on to the next digit.
The number is **5739**, which is 2160 greater than 3579 (160 more than the 2000 specified).
The next closest is 5397, which is 1818 greater than 3579 (172 less than the 2000 specified).

In order to have a number that is 4000 greater than 3579, start with the digit 7. The new number is **7593**, which is 4014 greater than 3579.

2. The next number has five digits: 21084.
Pupils will need to begin with the digit 1 to find a number that is half of 21084.
The nearest number is **10428**. Half of 21084 is 10542, so the new number is 114 less.

Pupils will need to begin with the digit 4 to find a number that is twice as big as 21084.
The nearest number is **42180**. Double 21084 is 42168, so the new number is only 12 more.

The pupils will need to begin with the digit 8 to find a number that is four times bigger than 21084. The nearest number is **84210**. Four times 21084 is 84336, so the new number is 126 less.

3. The final number has six digits: 135920.
Pupils will need to begin with the digit 9 to find a number that is seven times greater than 135920. The nearest number is **951320**. Seven times 135920 is 951440, so the new number is 120 less.

This activity can be extended to seven-digit numbers. For example, rearrange the digits 1, 2, 3, 4, 5, 6, 7 to make a number that is twice or three times as big.

Pupils can write their own number and rearrange the digits to make fractions (quarter, half, three quarters) or multiples of their original number.

Rearrange the digits

Here is a three-digit number: **1 2 3**.

The digits can be moved around, or rearranged, to make different numbers, such as 132, 312 and 231.
Can a second number be made that is about 100 greater than 123?
The closest is 231. The difference between 231 and 123 is 108, which is 8 more than 100.
The next closest is 213. The difference between 213 and 123 is 90, which is 10 less than 100.

1. Here is a four-digit number: **3 5 7 9**.

Rearrange the digits to make a number
that is about 2000 greater than 3579.   _____

Rearrange the digits to make a number
that is about 4000 greater than 3579.   _____

2. Here is a five-digit number: **2 1 0 8 4**.

Rearrange the digits to make a number
that is about half of 21084.   _____

Rearrange the digits to make a number
that is about twice as big as 21084.   _____

Rearrange the digits to make a number
that is about four times bigger than 21084.   _____

3. Here is a six-digit number: **1 3 5 9 2 0**.

Rearrange the digits to make a number
that is about seven times bigger than 135920.   _____

Multiplication and division, money and 'real-life' situations

Learning objectives

◆ Use brackets to simplify calculations.

Resources

AS 'Multiplying in Ancient Egypt'

Teacher's notes

This method of multiplying works because any number can be expressed by numbers that are powers of 2.

Any number to the power 0 is equal to 1. For example, $5^0 = 1$ and $10^0 = 1$.

Any number to the power 1 is equal to the number itself. For example, $8^1 = 8$ and $12^1 = 12$.

$2^0 = 1$ $2^1 = 2$ $2^2 = 4$ $2^3 = 8$ $2^4 = 16$ $2^5 = 32$ $2^6 = 64$ and so on.

So $25 = 16 + 8 + 1$ and $99 = 64 + 32 + 2 + 1$.

An example is provided and then there is a partially completed calculation.

Since $19 = 1 + 2 + \mathbf{16}$, $35 \times 19 = (35 \times \mathbf{1}) + (35 \times \mathbf{2}) + (35 \times \mathbf{16})$.
So $35 \times 19 = \mathbf{35 + 70 + 560 = 665}$.

When calculating 31×25 it is easier to double 25.
With 31×25 or   25 x 31
                        25 x   1 =   25
                        25 x   2 =   50
                        25 x   4 = 100
                        25 x   8 = 200
                        25 x 16 = 400
                             31   775

So **25 x 31 = 25 + 50 + 100 + 200 + 400 = 775**.

When calculating 90×64 it is easier to double 90. Furthermore, the doubling continues to exactly 64.
With 90×64 90 x   1 =   90
                     90 x   2 =   180
                     90 x   4 =   360
                     90 x   8 =   720
                     90 x 16 = 1440
                     90 x 32 = 2880
                     90 x 64 = 5760

So **90 x 64 – 5760**.

Try using this method with larger numbers, such as 150×97 and 279×742.
Ask pupils which numbers they would double.

Multiplying in Ancient Egypt

In Ancient Egypt two numbers were multiplied by a method of doubling and then adding.

Example: 20 x 12

Start by multiplying by 1:	20 x 1 = 20
Double this number:	20 x 2 = 40
Double again:	20 x 4 = 80
Double again:	20 x 8 = 160

Stop here because the next step would be 20 x 16, and 16 is greater than 12.

Since 12 = 4 + 8, then 20 x 12 = (20 x 4) + (20 x 8).
Look again at the example to see the answers to 20 x 4 and 20 x 8. Then add together the two products, 80 + 160.
Therefore, 20 x 12 = 80 + 160 = 240.

● Try this method with **35 x 19**.

Start by multiplying by 1:	35 x 1 =
Double this number:	35 x 2 =
Double again:	35 x 4 =
Double again:	35 x 8 =
Double again:	35 x 16 =

Stop here. Why?

_____

● 19 = 1 + 2 + _____. So 35 x 19 = (35 x _____) + (35 x ___) + (35 x _____).

Add the three products to get the answer.

_____

● On a blank sheet of paper, use this method to calculate these products:
31 x 25 and 90 x 64.

Challenge

● Explain how this method of multiplying works.

'Real-life' problems, checking results and using a calculator

Learning objectives

◆ Use pencil and paper methods for addition to solve 'real-life' problems.
◆ Use a calculator to check results.

Resources

AS 'Missing digits (1)'

Teacher's notes

In this problem-solving activity pupils put the digits 2 or 5 in each empty box to complete the addition equations.

In the example provided, there are two possible solutions: 22 + 55 = 77 and 25 + 52 = 77. Try to let pupils work out that having 7 as the units digit in the sum means that 2 and 5 have been added. Therefore, the two-digit numbers being added must end in 2 and 5 respectively. The tens digits also add up to 7, so the numbers must begin with 2 and 5.

Similar reasoning can be used to solve the other equations.

1. To produce 184:
The units digit is 4, so 2 + 2 = 4. To get the tens digit 8, 5 is added to 3.
The solution is **152 + 32 = 184**.

2. To produce 500:
To reach 0 as the tens digit, both the two middle digits must be 5. This means that 1 is carried.
The solution is **250 + 250 = 500**.

3. To produce 99:
The units digit is made by adding 2, 2 and 5. The tens digit is made in the same way.
There are two solutions: **22 + 22 + 55 = 99** and **25 + 22 + 52 = 99**.

4. To produce 300:
The sum ends in 0, so the two missing units digits must both be 5. This means that 1 is carried.
The three tens digits must add up to 9 to ensure that when the carried 1 is added a 0 is produced. Therefore, the three tens digits must be 5, 2 and 2.
There are two solutions: **25 + 25 + 250 = 300** and **55 + 25 + 220 = 300**.

5. To produce 1005:
The sum ends in 5, so the three units digits must each end in 5. One is carried. The three tens digits must add up to 9 to ensure that when the carried 1 is added a 0 is produced. Therefore, the three tens digits are 2, 2 and 5. One is carried again. Similarly, the three hundreds digits must also be 2, 2 and 5.
There are two solutions: **225 + 225 + 555 = 1005** and **225 + 255 + 525 = 1005**.

In the final equation each of the two numbers being added must begin with 55. The sum will then exceed 11 000.
There are many solutions such as: **5555 + 5555 = 11110; 5555 + 5552 = 11107; 5552 + 5552 = 11104**.

Missing digits (1)

This is a number sentence that has four missing digits. The digits 2 and 5 are put in the empty boxes to complete the number sentence.

$$\square\square + \square\square = 77$$

Put 2, 2, 5 and 5 in the boxes so that 22 + 55 = 77.

● Complete these number sentences by putting 2 or 5 in each empty box.

1. $\boxed{1}\ \square\ \square + \boxed{3}\ \square = 184$

2. $\square\ \square\ \boxed{0} + \square\ \square\ \boxed{0} = 500$

3. $\square\ \square + \square\ \square + \square\ \square = 99$

4. $\square\ \square + \square\ \square + \square\ \square\ \boxed{0} = 300$

5. $\square\ \square\ \square + \square\ \square\ \square + \square\ \square\ \square = 1005$

Challenge

● How many solutions can you find for this number sentence?

$\square\ \square\ \square\ \square + \square\ \square\ \square\ \square =$ a number greater than 11 000.

Fractions and decimals

Learning objectives

◆ Order fractions in ascending/descending order.
◆ Change a simple fraction to a decimal and back.

Resources

AS 'True or false?'

Teacher's notes

In this activity pupils read each statement and decide whether it is true or false. Then they explain why they came to this decision.

The first four statements are about the equivalence of fractions and decimals.

1. False. $\frac{1}{3}$ is equal to 0.33 and is, therefore, slightly more than 0.3. One way to explain the difference is to multiply each number by 3. $\frac{1}{3}$ x 3 = 1, whereas 0.3 x 3 = 0.9. So 0.3 must be less than $\frac{1}{3}$.

2. True. $\frac{1}{4}$ = 0.25, which is greater than 0.2. This time, multiply each number by 4. $\frac{1}{4}$ x 4 = 1, whereas 0.2 x 4 = 0.8. So $\frac{1}{4}$ is greater than 0.2.

3. False. There are different ways of comparing the two numbers. 0.75 = $\frac{3}{4}$ = $\frac{9}{12}$, whereas $\frac{2}{3}$ = $\frac{8}{12}$. So 0.75 is the larger number. Alternatively, multiply each number by 4. 0.75 x 4 = 3, whereas $\frac{2}{3}$ x 4 = $\frac{8}{3}$ which is less than 3 ($\frac{9}{3}$).

4. True. 0.8 = $\frac{8}{10}$ = $\frac{16}{20}$.

5. True. $\frac{6}{10}$ = $\frac{3}{5}$.

6. False. 12 x $\frac{1}{3}$ = 4, which is less than 6. There are 18 thirds in 6.

7. False. Each fraction and decimal are converted to fractions of 16 so they can be compared.

0.25 = $\frac{1}{4}$ = $\frac{4}{16}$; $\frac{5}{8}$ = $\frac{10}{16}$; 0.5 = $\frac{8}{16}$; $\frac{7}{8}$ = $\frac{14}{16}$; 0.75 = $\frac{3}{4}$ = $\frac{12}{16}$.

The sequence in fractions of 16 becomes: $\frac{4}{16}$, $\frac{3}{16}$, $\frac{10}{16}$, $\frac{8}{16}$, $\frac{14}{16}$, $\frac{12}{16}$.

The sequence in increasing order is: $\frac{3}{16}$, $\frac{4}{16}$, $\frac{8}{16}$, $\frac{10}{16}$, $\frac{12}{16}$, $\frac{14}{16}$.

The solution is: $\frac{3}{16}$, **0.25, 0.5,** $\frac{5}{8}$, **0.75,** $\frac{7}{8}$.

True or false?

● Read the statements, decide whether each is true or false and put a circle around your answers. Then explain your answers.

1. $\frac{1}{3}$ is equal to 0.3.   **True/False**

_____

2. $\frac{1}{4}$ is more than 0.2.   **True/False**

_____

3. 0.75 is less than $\frac{2}{3}$.   **True/False**

_____

4. 0.8 is equal to $\frac{16}{20}$.   **True/False**

_____

5. There are 6 tenths in $\frac{3}{5}$.   **True/False**

_____

6. There are 12 thirds in 6.   **True/False**

_____

7. This sequence of fractions and decimals is in
order of increasing size from left to right:
0.25, $\frac{3}{16}$, $\frac{5}{8}$, 0.5, $\frac{7}{8}$, 0.75.   **True/False**

Explain your answer.

_____

_____

_____

_____

Fractions and decimals

Learning objectives

◆ Find what must be added to a mixed number or fraction to make a whole number.
◆ Relate fractions to division.

Resources

AS 'Fraction sentences'

Teacher's notes

In this problem-solving activity pupils use a set of digits to make fractions that satisfy the equations. Remind pupils that 1 is not used in this activity and that each digit can be used only once in every equation.

1. Try the following strategy to help reduce the time spent in selecting the digits.
In the first equation two fractions are added to make 2.
This sum can be made in various ways: $\frac{1}{2} + 1\frac{1}{2}$; $\frac{2}{3} + 1\frac{1}{3}$; $\frac{1}{3} + 1\frac{2}{3}$; $\frac{1}{4} + 1\frac{3}{4}$; $\frac{3}{4} + 1\frac{1}{4}$.
Encourage pupils to look for different ways of producing these pairs of fractions.

Seven possible solutions:

$\frac{2}{4} + \frac{9}{6} = 2 \ (\frac{1}{2} + 1\frac{1}{2})$ $\frac{2}{6} + \frac{5}{3} = 2 \ (\frac{1}{3} + 1\frac{2}{3})$

$\frac{4}{8} + \frac{9}{6} = 2 \ (\frac{1}{2} + 1\frac{1}{2})$ $\frac{2}{8} + \frac{7}{4} = 2 \ (\frac{1}{4} + 1\frac{3}{4})$

$\frac{2}{3} + \frac{8}{6} = 2 \ (\frac{2}{3} + 1\frac{1}{3})$ $\frac{6}{8} + \frac{5}{4} = 2 \ (\frac{3}{4} + 1\frac{1}{4})$

$\frac{6}{9} + \frac{4}{3} = 2 \ (\frac{2}{3} + 1\frac{1}{3})$

2. A sum of 3 can be made in various ways: $1\frac{1}{2} + 1\frac{1}{2}$; $\frac{1}{2} + 2\frac{1}{2}$; $\frac{1}{3} + 2\frac{2}{3}$; $\frac{2}{3} + 2\frac{1}{3}$; $\frac{3}{4} + 2\frac{1}{4}$.

Six possible solutions:

$\frac{3}{2} + \frac{9}{6} = 3 \ (1\frac{1}{2} + 1\frac{1}{2})$ $\frac{2}{6} + \frac{8}{3} = 3 \ (\frac{1}{3} + 2\frac{2}{3})$

$\frac{4}{8} + \frac{5}{2} = 3 \ (\frac{1}{2} + 2\frac{1}{2})$ $\frac{4}{6} + \frac{7}{3} = 3 \ (\frac{2}{3} + 2\frac{1}{3})$

$\frac{3}{6} + \frac{5}{2} = 3 \ (\frac{1}{2} + 2\frac{1}{2})$ $\frac{6}{8} + \frac{9}{4} = 3 \ (\frac{3}{4} + 2\frac{1}{4})$

3. The next equation involves subtracting one fraction from another. A difference of 2 can be achieved in various ways: $4 - 2$; $3\frac{1}{2} - 1\frac{1}{2}$; $2\frac{2}{3} - \frac{2}{3}$; $2\frac{1}{3} - \frac{1}{3}$; $2\frac{1}{2} - \frac{1}{2}$; $2\frac{1}{4} - \frac{1}{4}$.

Six possible solutions:

$\frac{8}{2} - \frac{6}{3} = 2 \ (4 - 2)$ $\frac{7}{3} - \frac{2}{6} = 2 \ (2\frac{1}{3} - \frac{1}{3})$

$\frac{7}{2} - \frac{6}{4} = 2 \ (3\frac{1}{2} - 1\frac{1}{2})$ $\frac{5}{2} - \frac{4}{8} = 2 \ (2\frac{1}{2} - \frac{1}{2})$

$\frac{8}{3} - \frac{4}{6} = 2 \ (2\frac{2}{3} - \frac{2}{3})$ $\frac{9}{4} - \frac{2}{8} = 2 \ (2\frac{1}{4} - \frac{1}{4})$

4. A difference of 1 can be achieved in many ways.

Some possible solutions:

$\frac{8}{2} - \frac{9}{3} \ (4 - 3)$ $\frac{9}{3} - \frac{8}{4}$ and $\frac{9}{3} - \frac{4}{2} \ (3 - 2)$ $\frac{5}{2} - \frac{6}{4} \ (2\frac{1}{2} - 1\frac{1}{2})$

$\frac{3}{2} - \frac{4}{8} \ (1\frac{1}{2} - \frac{1}{2})$ $\frac{8}{6} - \frac{3}{9}$ and $\frac{4}{3} - \frac{2}{6} \ (1\frac{1}{3} - \frac{1}{3})$ $\frac{5}{3} - \frac{6}{9} \ (1\frac{2}{3} - \frac{2}{3})$

$\frac{5}{4} - \frac{2}{8} \ (1\frac{1}{4} - \frac{1}{4})$ $\frac{7}{4} - \frac{6}{8}(1\frac{3}{4} - \frac{3}{4})$

Fraction sentences

In these number sentences a digit is missing from each empty box.

● The digits **2 3 4 5 6 7 8 9** can be used only once in each number sentence.
Do not use **1**.

1. Try to find five solutions for this number sentence.

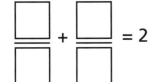

$$\frac{\square}{\square} + \frac{\square}{\square} = 2 \qquad \frac{\square}{\square} + \frac{\square}{\square} = 2 \qquad \frac{\square}{\square} + \frac{\square}{\square} = 2$$

$$\frac{\square}{\square} + \frac{\square}{\square} = 2 \qquad \frac{\square}{\square} + \frac{\square}{\square} = 2$$

2. Try to find three solutions for this number sentence.

$$\frac{\square}{\square} + \frac{\square}{\square} = 3 \qquad \frac{\square}{\square} + \frac{\square}{\square} = 3 \qquad \frac{\square}{\square} + \frac{\square}{\square} = 3$$

3. Try to find three solutions for this number sentence.

$$\frac{\square}{\square} - \frac{\square}{\square} = 2 \qquad \frac{\square}{\square} - \frac{\square}{\square} = 2 \qquad \frac{\square}{\square} - \frac{\square}{\square} = 2$$

4. This number sentence has many solutions. How many can you find?

$$\frac{\square}{\square} - \frac{\square}{\square} = 1$$

Handling data

Learning objectives

- Use mode, range and median confidently.
- Represent data.
- Interrogate given data.

Resources

AS 'Favourite take-aways'

Teacher's notes

This activity is about analysing and interrogating data.

Pupils are presented with a table of the results from a survey on take-away meals. They first have to complete the '**Totals**' column.

Results

Pizza	**85**
Fish and chips	**111**
Indian meal	**59**
Chinese meal	**77**
Burger	**68**

Ask pupils how they might check whether these totals are correct. One solution is to add the five totals to produce 400.

Solutions
1. The most popular take-away meal is **fish and chips**.
2. The least popular is an **Indian meal**.
3. The range of the totals is **111 – 59 = 52**.
4a. The median for the totals is **77**.
4b. **The Chinese meal**.
5. The greatest range is shown with the **over 61** group; 65 – 4 = 61.
6. The smallest range is shown with the **31–60 group**; 26 – 9 = 17.
7. For people under 61 the most popular take-away is a **Chinese meal** with **71**. Next is pizza with 67.
8. The reason that a Chinese meal is not the most popular take-away overall is due to the large number of over 61 people voting for fish and chips. Out of 100 people over 61, 65 voted for fish and chips.

Favourite take-aways

400 people of different ages are asked to name their favourite take-away meal. The results of the survey are in the table below.

Take-away	Under 16	16–30	31–60	Over 61	Totals
Pizza	26	22	19	18	
Fish and chips	13	11	22	65	
Indian meal	8	23	24	4	
Chinese meal	16	29	26	6	
Burger	37	15	9	7	

● Complete the '**Totals**' column in the table.

1. Overall, which is the most popular take-away? _____

2. Overall, which is the least popular take-away? _____

3. What is the range of the totals? _____

4a. What is the median for the totals? _____

4b. Which meal is this? _____

The data from different age groups have different ranges.

5. Which age group has the greatest range? _____

6. Which age group has the smallest range? _____

7. For people under 61 which take-away is most popular? _____

8. Explain why this take-away is not the most popular overall. _____

_____

Calculator skills

Learning objectives

- ◆ Gain familiarity with calculator functions.
- ◆ Clear the calculator display.
- ◆ Use the +, –, x, ÷, = keys to calculate.

Resources

AS 'Closest estimate'
Calculators

Teacher's notes

In this activity pupils use mental calculation to estimate a product. Then they select a number from a list of five that they think is closest to the answer. Finally, pupils check their choice by using a calculator to work out the exact product.

In the example provided, since 51 x 19 can be approximated to 50 x 20, the product must be about 1000. A good guess would be to choose 980 from the list of five numbers. The exact product is 969, so 980 is closest.

1. 214 x 31 can be approximated to 220 x 30 = 6600. Choose **6700**. The exact product is **6634**, so 6700 is closest.

2. 87 x 26 can be approximated to 88 x 25. When multiplying by 25 add two zeros and divide by four. So 88 x 25 = 8800 ÷ 4 = 2200. Choose **2300**. The exact product is **2262**, so 2300 is closest.

3. (21 + 12) x 900 is equal to 33 x 900. Since 33 is about one third of 100, add two zeros and divide by three. So 33 x 900 approximates to 90 000 ÷ 3 = 30 000. Choose **30 000**. The exact product is **29 700**, so 30 000 is closest.

4. (50 + 25) x 66 is equal to (50 x 66) + ($\frac{1}{2}$ x 50 x 66). To find 50 x 66 add two zeros and divide by two. So 50 x 66 = 6600 ÷ 2 = 3300. And 25 x 66 is half of this, which is about 1600. Together they equal 4900. Choose **5000**. The exact product is **4950** so 5000 is closest.

5. (198 + 189) x 206 approximates to (200 + 200) x 200 = 400 x 200 = 80 000. Choose **80 000**. The exact product is **79 722**, so 80 000 is closest.

Ask pupils to devise their own products to try out on their friends.

Closest estimate

- Estimate the answer by mental calculation.
- Underline the number that you think is closest to the answer.
- Then check the calculation using a calculator.

Example:

> **51 x 19.** Which is closest? 100   900   980   1050   1090
> 51 x 19 is close to 50 x 20, which equals 1000.
> So 980 would be a good guess at being closest to 51 x 19.
> Underline 980.
> Check the calculation using a calculator.

1. 214 x 31. Which is closest? 660   7000   6700   6000   63 000

What is the exact answer? _____

Was your estimate correct? _____

2. 87 x 26. Which is closest? 240   2300   2000   19 000   2500

What is the exact answer? _____

Was your estimate correct? _____

3. (21 + 12) x 900. Which is closest? 2700   30 000   29 000   300 000   3000

What is the exact answer? _____

Was your estimate correct? _____

4. (50 + 25) x 66. Which is closest? 5000   50 000   49 000   540 490

What is the exact answer? _____

Was your estimate correct? _____

5. (198 + 189) x 206. Which is closest? 8000   820 000   80 000   880   7800

What is the exact answer? _____

Was your estimate correct? _____

Properties of 2-D shapes

Learning objectives

- ◆ Identify properties and features of 2-D shapes.
- ◆ Work systematically.

Resources

AS 'Inside a triangle'

Teacher's notes

In this activity pupils have to follow the instructions to construct the largest possible square inside each of two triangles.

Pupils will require blank paper, a ruler and a sharp pencil to draw fine lines. Encourage them to draw lightly and not press down too hard.

- **Triangle A** is a right-angled triangle. Constructing two squares at the right-angle is relatively easy. Care needs to be taken, however, to ensure that the squares are properly aligned and that the line passes exactly through their corners.

- **Triangle B** is an equilateral triangle. To complete the construction, pupils should draw in the final square. The sides of this square are about 3.2cm. Ask them to measure the four sides of the square. This checks that a proper square has been constructed.

The construction can be started from any corner but it is probably less confusing if it is started from the left-hand corner of each triangle. Pupils can construct squares with sides of 1cm, 2cm or 3cm.

Triangle C is at an angle to the horizontal. Pupils should turn the sheet so the bottom side is horizontal. This makes it easier to draw the squares. The largest square has a side of almost **4.8cm**.

Pupils might like to find out if the same results are achieved when the squares are constructed from different corners of a triangle.
Are the largest squares the same size?
Are the largest squares in exactly the same positions inside each triangle or have their positions changed?

Inside a triangle

The aim is to draw the largest possible square inside a right-angled triangle.

- Copy **Triangle A** and construct two small squares 1 and 2.
- Draw a line from the right-angle of the triangle, through the corners of the two squares. This line meets the side of the triangle at the corner of the largest possible square. Draw this square.

Triangle A

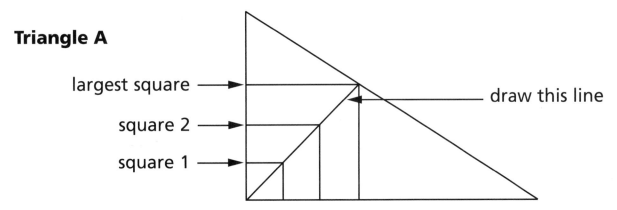

- The same method can be used with an equilateral triangle. Complete the construction of the largest possible square inside **Triangle B**.

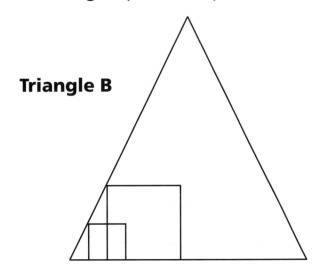

Triangle B

- Construct the largest possible square inside **Triangle C**.

Triangle C
Length of side of largest square = _____ cm.

Area and perimeter

Learning objectives

- ◆ Apply the formula for area to written problems.
- ◆ Convert units.
- ◆ Use conversions to help solve problems.

Resources

AS 'Dividing a square'

Teacher's notes

This problem-solving activity involves working out the areas into which a square is divided. There are two 8cm x 8cm squares, each of which has been divided into four different parts.

Pupils first calculate the area of the square, which is 8cm x 8cm = **64cm²**. It is important to know this because it is used as a check. The areas of the four parts should add up to the area of the complete square. Pupils should understand this.

When working out the areas of each part, there is no need to start with A and then go on to B, C and D. With the first square, start with B. Pupils will have to measure the side of square B, which is 4cm. Hence, it is one quarter of the large square.

So the area of B is 64cm² ÷ 4 = **16cm²**.
Triangle C is also one quarter, so its area is also **16cm²**.
Triangle A is half the area of square B. Its area is **8cm²**.
Shape D, which is a trapezium, is equal to the areas of B + A. Its area is, therefore, **24cm²**.

Add the four areas: 16cm² + 16cm² + 8cm² + 24cm² = 64cm².

If pupils have difficulty in seeing that the area of D equals the combined areas of B and A tell them to extend the vertical line that divides A and B. They will see that D is then divided into two areas that are mirror images of A and B.

With the second square, start with triangle D. Pupils should measure the side of triangle D, which is 4cm. Since triangle D is half of a square 4cm x 4cm, its area is half 16cm², which is 8cm². This is one eighth of the area of the large square.

So the area of triangle D = **8cm²**.
The areas C and D together equal half the area of the large square (64cm² ÷ 2).
So the areas of C + D = 32cm². If D is 8cm² then C must be **24cm²**.

Triangle A is half the area of triangle D. So its area is **4cm²**.
Finally, the combined areas of B and A are equal to half the area of the square, so the area of B is 32cm² – 4cm² = **28cm²**.

Add the four areas: 8cm² + 24cm² + 4cm² + 28cm² = 64cm².

If pupils have difficulty seeing that A is half the area of triangle D, tell them to extend the line forming the left-hand side of A until it meets the right-hand side of the square. The triangle formed is equal in area to D. It is also equal to twice the area of A.

Dividing a square

Here is an 8cm x 8cm square that has been divided into four parts: A, B, C, D.

- Calculate the following.

  The area of the square = _____ cm²

  The areas of each part.

  A = _____ cm²

  B = _____ cm²

  C = _____ cm²

  D = _____ cm²

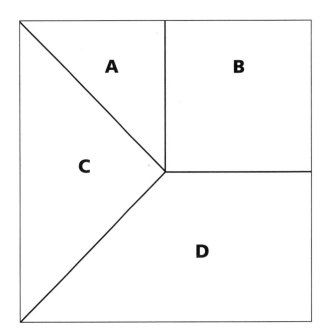

- How did you find the area of D? _____

_____

This is another 8cm x 8cm square.

- Find the following areas.

  A = _____ cm²

  B = _____ cm²

  C = _____ cm²

  D = _____ cm²

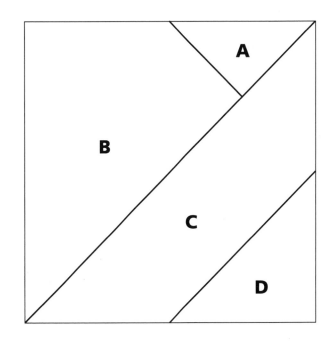

- How did you find the area of C? _____

_____

Angle and rotation

Learning objectives

◆ Use a set square.
◆ Measure accurately.

Resources

AS 'Straight line curves'
Set square and ruler
Squared graph paper

Teacher's notes

In this design activity pupils are shown how to construct three curved shapes from straight lines.

The shapes are a spiral, a circle and a parabola.

Provide pupils with squared graph paper so that they can draw these shapes for themselves. Emphasise the need for care and tidiness in order to achieve the best effects.

Once a shape has been created it can be emphasised by drawing carefully around the envelope of straight lines with a pen or coloured pencil. Pupils can leave the construction lines in place. These can become part of the overall design.

Straight line curves

Here are three curved shapes that can be drawn using straight lines.

A spiral

start

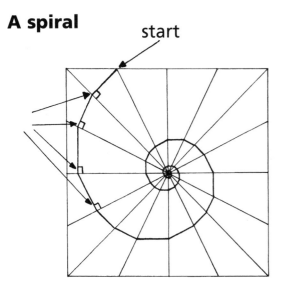

- First draw a square.
  Then draw a number of straight lines passing through the centre.

  Start on the edge of the square. Use a set square to join pairs of straight lines by short thick lines to make right-angles.

  The short lines turn inwards towards the centre. A spiral is formed.

A circle

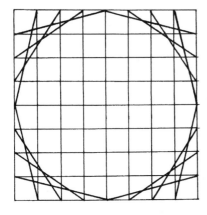

- Draw a square on your graph paper.

  Draw lines between the squares of your graph paper on the top and bottom and those on the sides. These straight joining lines merge to form a circle.

This is a curve which looks like half an egg.

A parabola

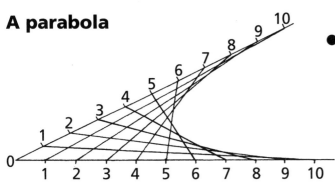

- Draw two straight lines that meet at an acute angle. Starting from where the lines meet, at 0, mark equal divisions along each line. These divisions might be 1cm apart. Join pairs of points on the two lines: 1 and 10, 2 and 9, 3 and 8, 4 and 7, 5 and 6.

- Use the three shapes to create a design of your own. Carefully plan out your design before beginning to draw the shapes. Your design could include a spiral inside a circle, a parabola joined to a circle, four or five spirals joined together, a cross created by drawing four parabolas at right-angles to each other, circles within circles or spirals within spirals.

Addition and subtraction

Learning objectives

◆ Apply a method of subtraction to written problems.

Resources

AS 'Missing digits (2)'

Teacher's notes

In this problem-solving activity pupils put the digits 2 or 5 in each empty box to complete the subtraction equations.

In the example provided, encourage pupils to see that to obtain 3 as the units digit in the result means that 2 has been subtracted from 5. Similarly, the tens digits differ by 3, so the numbers begin with 5 and 2.

Similar reasoning can be used to solve the other equations.

1. In the first equation the digit 2 must be subtracted from 5 to get 3 as the units digit. To obtain 7 as the tens digit, 5 must be subtracted from 12. The equation is **125 – 52** = 73.

2. In the next equation 0 is subtracted from 2 to get 2 as the units digit. The hundreds digit must be 5 in order to get 28 as the first two digits: 50 – 22 = 28 is the only possible solution. The equation is **502 – 220** = 282.

3. To get 2 as the result of the third equation the first two-digit number must begin with 5. The two-digit numbers being subtracted must each begin with 2. The equation is **52 – 25 – 25** = 2.

4. Because the fourth equation ends in two zeros, the numbers being subtracted must both end in 22 or 55. The only way to get 17 from these digits is 22 – 5. The equation is **2222 – 522** = 1700 or **2255 – 555** = 1700.

5. In the last equation, the four-digit number must begin with 5. The hundreds digit must also be 5. Having realised this, it is now a matter of systematically going through the possible combinations.

Here are six possible solutions:

5555 – 222 = 5333   **5552 – 222 = 5330**
5555 – 225 = 5330   **5552 – 225 = 5327**
5555 – 252 = 5303   **5525 – 222 = 5303**

Missing digits (2)

This number sentence has four missing digits. The digits 2 and 5 are put in the empty boxes to complete the number sentence.

$$\boxed{}\,\boxed{}-\boxed{}\,\boxed{} = 33$$

Put 5, 5, 2 and 2 in the boxes so that 55 – 22 = 33.

● Complete these number sentences by putting 2 or 5 in each empty box.

1. $\boxed{1}\,\boxed{}\,\boxed{}-\boxed{}\,\boxed{} = 73$

2. $\boxed{}\,\boxed{0}\,\boxed{}-\boxed{}\,\boxed{}\,\boxed{0} = 282$

3. $\boxed{}\,\boxed{}-\boxed{}\,\boxed{}-\boxed{}\,\boxed{} = 2$

● Find two solutions for this number sentence.

4. $\boxed{}\,\boxed{}\,\boxed{}\,\boxed{}-\boxed{}\,\boxed{}\,\boxed{} = 1700$

$\boxed{}\,\boxed{}\,\boxed{}\,\boxed{}-\boxed{}\,\boxed{}\,\boxed{} = 1700$

● How many solutions can you find for this number sentence?

5. $\boxed{}\,\boxed{}\,\boxed{}\,\boxed{}-\boxed{}\,\boxed{}\,\boxed{} =$ a number greater than 5300.

Challenge

● Make up a subtraction sentence of your own. Ask a friend to solve it.

Properties of numbers

Learning objectives

◆ Identify prime numbers.

Resources

AS 'Prime search'

Teacher's notes

This activity focuses on some interesting aspects of prime numbers.

In the first part, pupils have to group two-digit prime numbers: those ending in 3, 7 and 9. The groups are: 13, 23, 43, 53, 73, 83; 17, 37, 47, 67, 97; 19, 29, 59, 79, 89.

In the second part, pupils are now introduced to EMIRPs. (EMIRP is PRIME reversed.) These are prime numbers that are still prime numbers when reversed. The paired example 13 and 31 is given. Pupils have to find the other three two-digit pairs of EMIRPs.
The pairs are: **17 and 71**; **37 and 73**; **79 and 97**.

There are fourteen pairs of three-digit EMIRPs that some pupils could be encouraged to discover. Three-digit EMIRPs include 107 and 701; 113 and 311; 149 and 941; and 157 and 751.

An EMIRP cannot begin with an even number or with 5 because when the number is reversed it becomes a non-prime number. For example, 29, 43, 61 and 89 are prime numbers but 92, 34, 16 and 98 are not. The latter are all even numbers and, therefore, divisible by 2. A prime number beginning with 5, such as 53, on reversal becomes 35. Any number ending in 5 is divisible by 5 and cannot be a prime number, except for 5 itself.

The final part is about testing a prime number rule.
Multiples of 4 to 100: 4, 8, 12, 16, 20, 24, 28, 32, 36, 40, 44, 48, 52, 56, 60, 64, 68, 72, 76, 80, 84, 88, 92, 96, 100.

Some prime numbers are:
7 (8 − 1); 11 (12 − 1); 19 (20 − 1); 29 (28 + 1); 37 (36 + 1); 43 (44 − 1); 53 (52 + 1); 61 (60 + 1); 73 (72 + 1); 83 (84 − 1); 97 (96 + 1).

It is obvious that the rule must be true because all prime numbers end in 1, 3, 7 or 9.

● A prime number ending in 1 is between a number ending in 0 and another ending in 2. One of these numbers must be divisible by 4.
● A prime number ending in 3 is between a number ending in 2 and another ending in 4. One of these numbers must be divisible by 4.
● A prime number ending in 7 is between a number ending in 6 and another ending in 8. One of these numbers must be divisible by 4.
● A prime number ending in 9 is between a number ending in 8 and another ending in 0. One of these numbers must be divisible by 4.

Prime search

Some two-digit prime numbers remain as prime numbers when their tens digits are changed.

Example:

> 11 is a prime number, so are 31, 41, 61 and 71.

- Find other groups of two-digit prime numbers that are like this.

  _____

  _____

An EMIRP is a prime number whether it is read from left to right or from right to left.

Example:

> 13 is a prime number and so is 31, which is 13 reversed.
> The numbers 13 and 31 are a pair of EMIRPs.

- There are three more pairs of two-digit numbers that are EMIRPs. Can you find them?

  _____

  _____

- An EMIRP must begin and end with 1, 3, 7 or 9.
  Why can an EMIRP not begin with 2, 4, 6, 8 or 5?

  _____

  _____

- Test some prime numbers to see if they follow this rule:

Every prime number, except 2, must be 1 more or 1 less than a multiple of 4.

_____

_____

_____

Place value, ordering and rounding

Learning objectives

♦ Use negative numbers confidently and accurately.
♦ Apply subtraction to negative numbers.

Resources

AS 'Subtraction triangles'

Teacher's notes

In this problem-solving activity pupils are presented with incomplete subtraction triangles that contain negative numbers. They have to find the missing numbers.

In the first triangle, the empty circle at the top must be a negative number because the difference between 4 and the missing number is 9. Furthermore, the difference between 3 and the missing number is 8. The missing number is **–5**. Pupils may find alternative solutions to some of the triangles.

The first two triangles are:

1.   **–5**   2.   –4
       9   8   7   9
   4   **1**   3   3   **2**   5

The next two triangles are different because they contain zeros. If a zero is in the middle then the two numbers at each corner must be the same.

The triangles are:

3.   **–2**   4.   **–1**
       0   5   0   **0**
   –2   **5**   3   –1   0   **–1**

The final triangle has two possible solutions:

            0   0
       2   4   2   4
   2   6   **–4**   **–2**   6   **4**

Subtraction triangles

In a subtraction triangle the number in the middle of each side is the difference of the two numbers at the two corners.

Example:

Two numbers are missing from the empty circles.
Put −1 and 6 in the circles.
$1 − (−1) = 2$; $7 − (−1) = 8$; $7 − 1 = 6$.

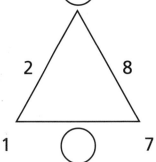

● Complete these subtraction triangles by finding the missing numbers.

1.

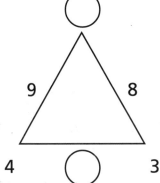

2.

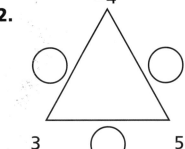

3.

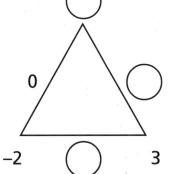

4.

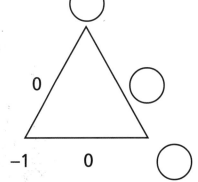

This subtraction triangle has two solutions.

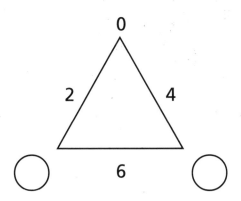

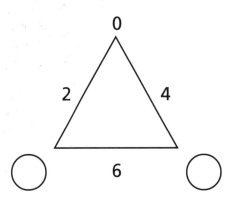

Mental calculation strategies

Learning objectives

- ◆ Understand a standard written method for long multiplication to TU x TU.
- ◆ Use a standard written method for long multiplication to solve problems.

Resources

AS 'The Nikhilam Sutra'
Calculator

Teacher's notes

This is a deficiency method in which addition and simple multiplication replace a longer and more difficult multiplication. This sutra, or rule, comes from Vedic mathematics and was probably devised over a thousand years ago. Pupils will need blank paper to work on.

This example shows why the method works.

88 x 97

	88(00)		(100 − 88)
+			x
	97(00)		(100 − 97)

=	185(00)	+	(100 x 100) − [(88 x 100) − (90 x 100)]	+ (88 x 97)
= 10 000 +	8500	+	10 000 − 18500	+ (88 x 97)
= 10 000 +	8500	+	10 000 − 10 000 − 8500	+ (88 x 97)
= 10 000				+ (88 x 97)

The two 10 000s and two 8500s cancel each other out.
The first digit, which equals 10 000, is ignored so the calculation equals 88 x 97.

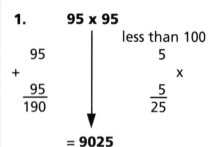

1. **95 x 95**

less than 100

```
  95          5
+            x
  95          5
 190         25
```

= 9025

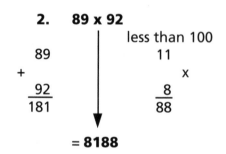

2. **89 x 92**

less than 100

```
  89         11
+            x
  92          8
 181         88
```

= 8188

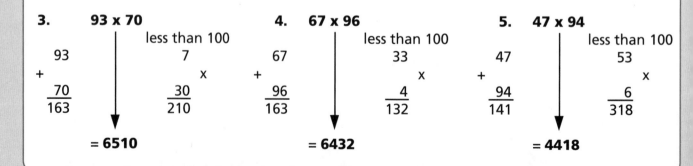

3. **93 x 70**

less than 100

```
  93          7
+            x
  70         30
 163        210
```

= 6510

4. **67 x 96**

less than 100

```
  67         33
+            x
  96          4
 163        132
```

= 6432

5. **47 x 94**

less than 100

```
  47         53
+            x
  94          6
 141        318
```

= 4418

The Nikhilam Sutra

Here is a method of multiplying numbers that was developed in India over a thousand years ago. It works well with numbers close to 100.

Example:

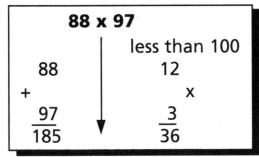

Add 10 000 to 185 = 18 500. Add the numbers 18 500 + 36 = 18 536. Ignore the first digit. The answer is 8536. Check this on a calculator.

● Use the method to find these products.

1. **95 x 95**

```
         |  less than 100
  95     |        5
+        |           x
  95     ▼        5
         ▼
```

2. **89 x 92**

```
         |  less than
         |  100
         ▼
         ▼
```

Check your answers using a calculator.

The calculation is slightly more difficult when the numbers are smaller.

Example:

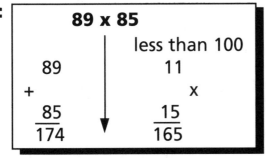

Add 10 000 to 174 = 17 400. Add the numbers 17 400 + 165 = 17 565. Ignore the first digit. The answer is 7565. Check this on a calculator.

● Use the method to find these products.

3. 93 x 70   **4.** 67 x 96   **5.** 47 x 94

Making decisions and checking results

Learning objectives

◆ Check results using an equivalent calculation.
◆ Use an inverse operation to check the accuracy of a calculation.

Resources

AS 'How do you know?'

Teacher's notes

This problem-solving activity covers a wide range of calculations involving all four operations. Pupils are presented with a series of calculations that have incorrect answers. They have to explain how they can tell the answer is wrong without carrying out the full calculation.

1. 25 + 70 + 65 + 55 cannot equal 210 because 5 + 5 + 5 = 15. The answer must end in 5.

2. The sum 18 + 28 + 38 + 48 + 58 must end in 0 since 5 x 8 = 40.

3. 1884 + 2769 + 3588 cannot end in an even number since two even numbers are being added to one odd number. The final digit of the sum must be an odd number.

4. 48 + 49 + 50 + 51 + 52 is the same as (48 + 52) + (49 + 51) + 50 or 100 + 100 + 50. So the sum cannot end in 5; it must end in 0.

5. The next equation can be reasoned in the same way. 35 + 45 = 80, 36 + 44 = 80 ... 39 + 41 = 80. The sum cannot end in 2; it must end in 0.

6. 1 x 1 x 1 = 1. The product 11 x 11 x 11 must end in 1.

7. 7 x 3 = 21. The product 197 x 153 must end in 1.

8. 97 is a prime number and cannot be divided by 7.

9. A number must end in 5 or 0 to be divisible by 5. So 67 596 cannot be divided by 5.

10. 100 ÷ 25 = 4. Any hundreds number such as 600, 1200 or 800 divided by 25 must give an answer that is a multiple of 4. The answer 33 is not a multiple of 4.

11. The digits of any number that can be divided by 9 also add up to 9 or a multiple of 9. 2430 has digits that add up to 9; it is therefore exactly divisible by 9 and there can be no remainder.

12. Similarly, the digits 891 add up to 18. It is exactly divisible by 9 so there is no remainder.

How do you know?

- Each of the following calculations is wrong. How can you tell quickly without carrying out the full calculation? Explain your reasons.

1. $25 + 70 + 65 + 55 = 210$

_____

2. $18 + 28 + 38 + 48 + 58 = 198$

_____

3. $1884 + 2769 + 3588 = 6356$

_____

4. $48 + 49 + 50 + 51 + 52 = 255$

_____

5. $35 + 36 + 37 + 38 + 39 + 40 + 41 + 42 + 43 + 44 + 45 = 442$

_____

6. $11 \times 11 \times 11 = 1330$

_____

7. $197 \times 153 = 30\ 147$

_____

8. $97 \div 7 = 14$

_____

9. $67\ 596 \div 5 = 13\ 519$

_____

10. $800 \div 25 = 33$

_____

11. $2430 \div 9 = 270\ r3$

_____

12. $891 \div 9 = 99\ r1$

_____

Ratio and proportion

Learning objectives

◆ Recognise vocabulary for ratio and proportion.
◆ Use ratio correctly.

Resources

AS 'Circles'

Teacher's notes

In this activity pupils are presented with a number of circles in a box. There are two kinds of circle, O and ●. Pupils have to work out the ratios and percentages of different circles as more are added or removed.

At the start there are **12** O and **8** ● making a total of **20** circles in the box.

For every 2 ● there are **3** O.

There are 20 circles in total so the O make up 5 x 12 = **60%** of the total.

The ● are $\frac{8}{20}$ or $\frac{2}{5}$ of the total.

5 ● are added so the new numbers are: 12 O, 13 ●, making a total of 25.

The O are now 4 x 12 = **48%** of the total.

For every 60 O there would be 5 x 13 = **65** ●.

5 O are removed. The new numbers are: 7 O, 13 ●, making a total of 20.

The O are now 5 x 7 = **35%** of the total remaining in the box.

Adding 8 ● means there will be 21 ● and 7 O. For every O there will be 3 ●. The ● will be $\frac{3}{4}$ or **75%** of the total.

This activity can be easily extended by suggesting that different numbers of circles are added and removed.

Pupils could be asked to devise questions of their own for others to answer.

Name: _____ **Date:** _____

Circles

The box contains two kinds of circle: O and ●.

- Count the circles in the box.

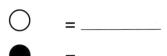 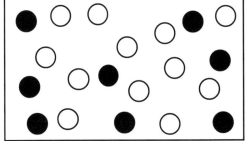

$$O \quad = \text{_____}$$

$$● \quad = \text{_____}$$

Total = _____

- Complete these sentences.

    For every 2 ● there are _____ O.

    The O are _____ % of the total circles in the box.

    The ● are this fraction of the total circles in the box. _____

- Add 5 ●. Draw these in the box.

    Complete these sentences.

    The O are now _____ % of the total circles in the box.

    For every 60 O there would be _____ ●.

- Remove 5 O by crossing them out like this, ⊠.

    Complete this sentence.

    The O are now _____ % of the total circles remaining in the box.

- How many ● must be added so that for every O there are 3 ●? _____

    What will be the % of ● in the box? _____

Maths for the More Able 5

Shape and space

Learning objectives

◆ Draw symmetrical shapes on a line that is not vertical.

Resources

AS 'Symmetrical patterns'

Teacher's notes

In this activity pupils have to complete patterns of shaded squares that are symmetrical about lines of symmetry.

The first two patterns are symmetrical about single lines of symmetry.

1. 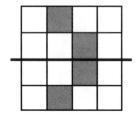   2.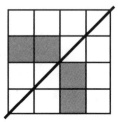

The next two patterns are symmetrical about two lines of symmetry. Starting with three squares the whole of grid 4 will become shaded.

3. 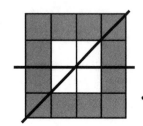   4.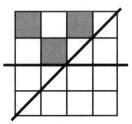

With larger grids it becomes more difficult to visualise the pattern.

5.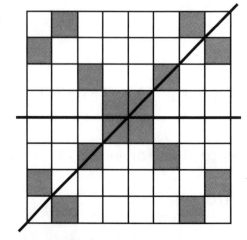

Name: _____ **Date:** _____

Symmetrical patterns

● Complete each pattern of shaded squares so that it is symmetrical about the line.

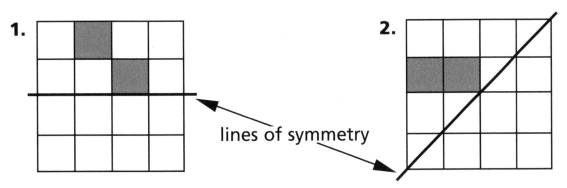

lines of symmetry

This pattern has two lines of symmetry.

Shade in three squares that will result in a symmetrical pattern where all the squares will become shaded.

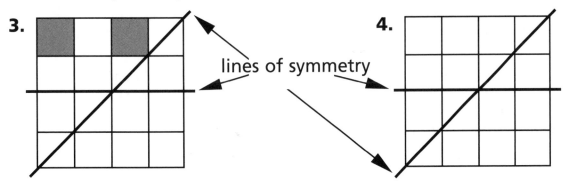

lines of symmetry

This pattern is more difficult to complete.

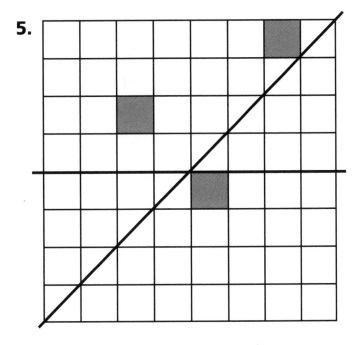

Shape and space

Learning objectives

- ◆ Know and use the term 'translation'.
- ◆ Carry out translations from given instructions.

Resources

AS 'Repeating patterns'
Square graph paper

Teacher's notes

This activity is about following and writing instructions to create patterns of black and white squares in a grid.

In the example given, pupils have to write a set of instructions to produce a similar pattern on the other side of the grid. Ensure that pupils can follow the instructions. Make sure they understand fully the action of the repeated instructions. The repeat instruction saves time and space when writing a set of instructions.

The pattern on the right hand side is created by:
start B, colour, up 1, left 1, colour, up 1, right 1
⌐ repeat ◄

The pattern in the second grid is created by: start B, colour, up 1, left 1, colour, up 2, left 2
repeat ◄

The instructions starting at A create this pattern.

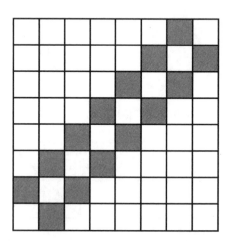

Many different patterns can be created. Pupils should experiment with different sets of instructions.

A pattern of squares going up then back down can be created using the following instructions.

Start, colour, up 1, right 1
repeat three times ◄

Then down 1, right 1, colour
repeat twice ◄

Repeating patterns

Here is a set of instructions that creates the pattern of shaded squares on the grid below.

Start A: colour, up 1, right 1, colour, up 1, left 1 ⌐
   ← —————— repeat ◄

- Write a set of instructions to produce a similar pattern on the right hand side.

Start B: _____

_____

_____

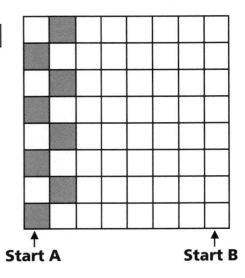

↑ **Start A**   ↑ **Start B**

- Work out the instructions that produce the pattern shown from Start B.

Start B: _____

_____

_____

- Draw a pattern following these instructions.

Start A: colour, up 1, left 1, colour, right 2 ⌐
   ← —————— repeat ◄

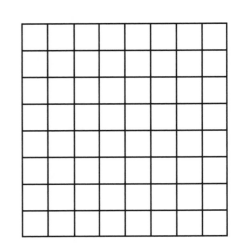

↑ **Start A**   ↑ **Start B**

- Create your own patterns.
  Write the instructions below.

_____

_____

_____

_____

Measures

Learning objectives

◆ Use metric conversions efficiently.
◆ Know basic imperial measures.
◆ Convert metric measures to imperial and vice versa.

Resources

AS 'Which one?'
Calculator

Teacher's notes

In this activity pupils convert from one measure to another to compare lengths, volumes and weights.

1. **Danielle** is the faster runner.
   A mile is further than 1.5km. A mile is 1760 yards and 1.5km is about 1500 x 1.1 yards = 1650 yards (1 metre is about 1.1 yards).

2. **Shop B** has the higher price.
   A yard is a shorter length than a metre, so £4 buys less material in shop B.

3. **Ahmed** is heavier.
   1kg equals 2.2lb, so 50kg = 50 x 2.2lb = 110lb.

4. **Shop D** is cheaper.
   1 kilogram = 2.2lb, so 0.5 kilogram = 1.1lb. Carrots at 40p/lb = 40p x 1.1 per half kilogram = 44p per half kilogram.

5. The **green bucket** has the greater capacity.
   1 litre is less than 2 pints, so 10 litres are less than 20 pints.

6. **Shop F** is more expensive because you could buy 2 one-pint tins for £4 and 2 pints are more than 1 litre.

Which one?

- Answer these questions. In each case, explain your answer.

1. Danielle can run 1 mile in 6 minutes.
Paul can run 1.5km in 6 minutes.

Who is the faster runner? _____

_____

2. Shop A sells curtain material at £4 per metre.
Shop B sells it at £4 per yard.

Which shop has the higher price? _____

_____

3. Billy weighs 50kg and Ahmed weighs 115lb.

Who is heavier? _____

_____

4. Shop C sells carrots at 45p per half kilogram.
Shop D sells them at 40p per lb.

Which shop is cheaper? _____

_____

5. A yellow bucket holds 10 litres.
A green bucket holds 20 pints.

Which bucket has the greater capacity? _____

_____

6. Shop E sells white paint at £2 for a one-pint tin.
Shop F sells the same white paint at £4 for a one-litre tin.

Which shop is more expensive? _____

_____

Measures, problems involving time

Learning objectives

- ◆ Establish the requirements of a written question.
- ◆ Use calculations of time within more complex written problems.
- ◆ Use the 24-hour clock confidently.

Resources

AS 'Wrong times'

Teacher's notes

In the first three parts of this activity pupils have to calculate the inaccuracy of some watches – how fast or slow each watch is. Ensure that pupils understand what is meant by fast and slow when applied to a watch.

1. Alan takes 15 minutes to walk to school and arrives there at 8:35. He left home at 8:20. Because Alan's watch read 8:25 it must be **5 minutes fast**.

2. Buvna takes 25 minutes to walk to school and arrives there at 8:50. She left home at 8:25. Because Buvna's watch read 8:15 it must be **10 minutes slow**.

3. Sean takes 18 minutes to walk to school and arrives there at 8:37. He left home at 8:19. Because Sean's watch read 8:30 it must be **11 minutes fast**.

4. Anna takes 22 minutes to walk to school, so she should leave at 8:23 to arrive by 8:45. Anna's watch read 8:23 + 8 minutes = **8:31**.

5a. Eric left home at 8:16 by his watch. The correct time was 8:16 + 12 minutes = 8:28. Eric arrives at school at 8:38 so his walk took **10 minutes**.

5b. **No**. It is not possible for Eric to leave home at 8:29 by his watch and arrive at school at 8:40 by the clock. The correct time on leaving home would be 8:29 + 12 minutes = 8:41. Eric cannot arrive at school before he leaves home!

Ask pupils to devise time problems for others to solve.

Wrong times

Three children leave their homes to walk to school in the morning. They check the times they leave home on their watches. On arriving at school they check the times on a large clock that is always exactly right. Each child has the wrong time on their watch.

● Work out by how much each watch is wrong. A watch might be slow or fast.

1. Alan leaves home at 8:25 by his watch. His walk to school takes 15 minutes. At school, the time on the clock is 8:35.
What conclusion can you come to about Alan's watch?

_____

2. Buvna leaves home at 8:15 by her watch. Her walk to school takes 25 minutes. At school, the time on the clock is 8:50.
What conclusion can you come to about Buvna's watch?

_____

3. Sean leaves home at 8:30 by his watch. His walk to school takes 18 minutes. At school, the time on the clock is 8:37.
What conclusion can you come to about Sean's watch?

_____

4. Anna has a watch that is 8 minutes fast, so it reads 8:08 when the correct time is 8:00. Anna takes 22 minutes to walk to school.
What time, by her watch, should Anna leave home to get to school at exactly 8:45 on the clock?

_____

5. Eric has a watch that is 12 minutes slow, so it reads 7:48 when the correct time is 8:00. Eric leaves home at 8:16 by his watch and arrives at school at 8:38 by the clock.

a. How long was his walk to school? _____

b. Is it possible for Eric to leave home at 8:29 by his watch and get to school at 8:40 by the clock?
Explain your answer. _____

_____

Pencil and paper procedures for addition and subtraction

Learning objectives

- ◆ Use formal and informal pencil and paper methods to record, support and explain additions and subtractions.
- ◆ Use standard written methods for addition and subtraction in the context of problem solving.

Resources

AS 'How does it work?'

Teacher's notes

In this activity pupils have to work out the methods by which some subtractions are done.

The first method employs decomposition in association with addition.

$$
482 = 200 + 282. \text{ So, } 482
$$

482	
− 143	can be rewritten as
339	

200 + 282 =	282
− 143	+ 57
57	339

Similarly, 560 = 300 + 260. So, 560

560	
− 160	can be rewritten as
400	

300 + 260 =	260
− 160	+ 140
140	400

Pupils are asked to turn two more subtractions into additions using the method described above.

768	=	568
− 196		+ 4
572		572

1682	=	1182
− 436		+ 64
1246		1246

The second method involves increasing both numbers by the same amount. The smaller number becomes a multiple of 100 (or 10 or 1000) and is then easier to subtract.

1225	add 124	1349
− 876	add 124	− 1000
349		349

7213	add 143	7356
− 5857	add 143	− 6000
1356		1356

Pupils have to carry out two subtractions using this method.

1095	add 34	1129
− 766	add 34	− 800
329		329

3781	add 8	3789
− 1492	add 8	− 1500
2289		2289

Pupils who carry out this work quickly can be presented with more difficult subtractions. For example, 7891 − 6175 and 289147 − 176788

Name: _____ **Date:** _____ AS

How does it work?

Look at these two calculations.

$$\begin{array}{r} 482 \\ -\ 143 \\ \hline 339 \end{array}$$ and $$\begin{array}{r} 282 \\ +\ 57 \\ \hline 339 \end{array}$$

The subtraction calculation can be rewritten as an addition to give the same answer.

Split 482 ⟶ 200 + 282
$$\begin{array}{r} -\ 143 \\ \hline 57 \end{array}$$
$$\begin{array}{r} 282 \\ +\ 57 \\ \hline 339 \end{array}$$

● Turn these three subtractions into additions by the same method.

$$\begin{array}{r} 560 \\ -\ 160 \\ \hline 400 \end{array}$$
$$\begin{array}{r} 768 \\ -\ 196 \\ \hline 572 \end{array}$$
$$\begin{array}{r} 1682 \\ -\ 436 \\ \hline 1246 \end{array}$$

Here is an interesting way of subtracting.

$$\begin{array}{r} 1225 \\ -\ 876 \end{array}$$ becomes $$\begin{array}{r} 1349 \\ -\ 1000 \\ \hline 349 \end{array}$$
$$\begin{array}{r} 7213 \\ -\ 5857 \end{array}$$ becomes $$\begin{array}{r} 7356 \\ -\ 6000 \\ \hline 1356 \end{array}$$

How does this method work?_____

_____

● Use the same method to calculate these two subtractions.

$$\begin{array}{r} 1095 \\ -\ 766 \end{array}$$
$$\begin{array}{r} 3781 \\ -\ 1492 \end{array}$$

Money and 'real-life' problems

Learning objectives

- ◆ Solve problems involving money.
- ◆ Choose an appropriate operation to solve 'real-life' money problems.
- ◆ Explain and record how a problem has been solved.

Resources

AS 'Buying and selling'

Teacher's notes

Explain the first question carefully so pupils understand what is being asked.

1. Start with a sum of £20. Work out 10% (£2) and subtract this from the £20. The new sum is £20 – £2 = £18. Work out 20% of £18 (£3.60) and subtract this from the £18. The final sum is £18 – £3.60 = £14.40.

   Now start with £20 and work out 20% (£4). Subtract this from the £20, £20 – £4 = £16. Work out 10% of £16 (£1.60) and subtract this from £16. The final sum is £16 – £1.60 = £14.40.
   So, Mr Haji is not correct. The answer would be the same if the 20% were calculated before the 10%.

   The following method uses algebra.
   Start with a sum A and subtract 10%: $A - 0.1A = 0.9A$.
   Subtract 20%: $0.9A - (0.9A \times 0.2) = 0.9A \times (1 - 0.2) = 0.9A \times 0.8$.
   Start with a sum A. Subtract 20%: $A - 0.2A = 0.8A$
   Subtract 10%: $0.8A - (0.8A \times 0.1) = 0.8A \times (1 - 0.1) = 0.8A \times 0.9$.

2. Des and Gary each sell **30 comics** (30/2 x 50p = £7.50 and 30/3 x 50p = £5.00). Des sells his comics at 50p for 2 = 25p per comic. Gary sells his at 50p for 3 = about 17p per comic.

   The average cost per comic is (25p + 17p) divided by 2 = about 21p per comic.
   If the pair sell 5 comics for £1.00 then the average cost per comic is 20p.
   Therefore, they make £12.00, which is less money than when Des and Gary sold their comics separately.

3. Sinead has 5p, 10p, 20p, 20p, 50p, £1. She uses the coins in the following ways to make the sums.
   5p, 10p, 5p + 10p, 20p, 5p + 20p, 10p + 20p, 5p + 10p + 20p, 20p + 20p, 5p + 20p + 20p, 10p + 20p + 20p.
   + 50p ... to £1.00
   + £1 ... to £1.50
   + £1 + 50p ... to £2.00 ... + 5p to £2.05.

4. Faraj has 1p, 2p, 2p, 5p, 10p, 10p. He uses the coins in the following ways to make the sums.
   1p, 2p, 1p + 2p, 2p + 2p, 5p, 1p + 5p, 2p + 5p, 1p + 2p + 5p, 2p + 2p + 5p, 1p + 2p + 2p + 5p.
   + 10p ... to 20p
   + 10p + 10p ... to 30p.

Buying and selling

1. Mr and Mrs Haji buy a kettle for £20 but there is 20% off in a sale. Because Mrs Haji has an account at the shop she also gets 10% off the sale price. Mr Haji is annoyed because the shop assistant first took off the 10% and then calculated 20% of what remained. He says the kettle would have been cheaper if the 20% had been taken off first and then 10% of what remained had been calculated. Is Mr Haji correct? **Yes/No**

Explain your answer. _____

_____

2. Des and Gary share a stall. Des sells his comics at 2 comics for 50p. Gary sells his comics at 3 comics for 50p.

On Friday Des makes £7.50 and Gary makes £5.00. How many comics did each of them sell?

Des sold _____ Gary sold _____

On Saturday Gary suggests that they work together and sell 5 comics for £1.00. They sell the same number of comics as on Friday.

How much did they make? _____

Explain why this is not the same amount as on Friday. _____

_____

3. Sinead has 6 coins in her pocket. Using only these 6 coins she says she can make every multiple of 5p from 5p to £2.05.

What 6 coins does Sinead have in her pocket? _____

_____

4. Faraj also has 6 coins in his pocket. He says he can use these to make every sum from 1p to 30p going up in 1p steps.

What 6 coins does Faraj have in his pocket? _____

_____

Properties of numbers and number sequences

Learning objectives

◆ Answer questions relating to square numbers.

Resources

AS 'Squares'
Calculator

Teacher's notes

This activity is in three parts. Parts 1 and 2 are about finding the squares of two-digit numbers ending in 5 and 1 respectively. Part 3 asks the pupils to explain a rule about squares.

1. The method used to find 25 x 25 can be explained in the following way.

25 x 25 = (20 + 5) x (20 + 5) = 20 x 20 + (5 x 20) + (5 x 20) + (5 x 5) = (20 + 5 + 5) x 20 + (5 x 5)
= (20 + 10) x 20 + (5 x 5) = (30 x 20) + (5 x 5) = 600 + 25 = 625.
   (2 + 1) x 2 + 5 x 5 = 3 x 2 + 5 x 5

2. The method used to find 31 x 31 can be explained as follows.

31 x 31 = (30 + 1) x (30 + 1) = 30 x 30 + (30 + 30 + 1) = 900 + 61 = 961.
                    3 x 3 + 30 + 61

The squares of 21 and 41 are found the same way, $21^2 = 441$; $41^2 = 1681$.

3. To find 51^2 or 61^2 the method is slightly different.
    Step 1: Subtract 1 from 51, so 51 − 1 = 50
    Step 2: Add 50 + 51 = 101
    Step 3: Square 5, so 5 x 5 = 25
    But 25 *joined* to 101 gives 25101. A calculator will show that 51 x 51 = 2601, so

$$\begin{array}{r} 25 \\ + \ \ 101 \\ \hline 2601 \end{array}$$

This also works for 61^2. Will pupils see the difference?

4. Explanation of the rule
Take two odd numbers **a** and **b**. Now $a^2 - b^2$ can be factorised as $(a + b)(a - b)$.
Since the two numbers are both odd then $(a + b)$ must be even and so must $(a - b)$.
The smallest pair of odd numbers are 1 and 3. Their product is $(1 + 3)(3 - 1) = 4 \times 2 = 8$.
All larger pairs of odd numbers must make products that are multiples of 8.

Squares

Here is an easy way to square two-digit numbers that end in 5.

Example:

> **25² or 25 x 25**
> Step 1: Add 1 to the tens digit (2), so 2 + 1 = 3.
> Step 2: Multiply the tens digit by 3 so 2 x 3 = 6.
> Step 3: Square 5, so 5 x 5 = 25.
> Step 4: Join 6 and 25 so the answer is 625.

Use a calculator to check the answer.

1. Square 45, 75 and 95 using this method. _____

How does the method work? _____

_____

Here is an easy way to square two-digit numbers that end in 1.

Example:

> **31² or 31 x 31**
> Step 1: Subtract 1 from 31, so 31 − 1 = 30.
> Step 2: Add 30 + 31 = 61.
> Step 3: Square 3, so 3 x 3 = 9.
> Step 4: Join the 9 and 61 so the answer is 961.

Use a calculator to check the answer.

2. Square 21 and 41 using this method. _____

3. Now try this method to square 51 and 61. What happens?

_____

Here is a rule about squares:

> *The difference of the two squares of any two odd numbers*
> *is always divisible by 8.*

4. Find a method to test this rule. _____

_____

Place value, ordering and rounding

Learning objectives

- ◆ Estimate and approximate when calculating.
- ◆ Round four-digit whole numbers to the nearest 10, 100 or 1000.

Resources

AS 'Matching pairs'

Teacher's notes

In the first part of this activity pupils are asked to estimate the products of multiplications and match each one with another number. Encourage pupils to look for simple number patterns, rather than trying mentally to calculate the answers.

1600 and **40 x 40** because 4 x 4 = 16.

115 and **23 x 5** because they are the smallest numbers and 20 x 5 = 100.

880 and **44 x 20** because 44 x 2 = 88.

62 500 and **250 x 250** because they are the largest numbers and 25 x 25 = 625.

3000 and **15 x 200** because 15 x 2 = 30.

2500 and **50 x 50** because 5 x 5 = 25.

In the second part pupils are asked to estimate the answers to addition and subtraction calculations and match them with statements.

Solutions

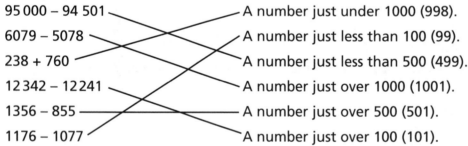

95 000 – 94 501 — A number just under 1000 (998).

6079 – 5078 — A number just less than 100 (99).

238 + 760 — A number just less than 500 (499).

12 342 – 12 241 — A number just over 1000 (1001).

1356 – 855 — A number just over 500 (501).

1176 – 1077 — A number just over 100 (101).

Matching pairs

The product of each multiplication in the bubble is equal to a number in the top box.

● Match up each pair by estimating the products in the bubble.

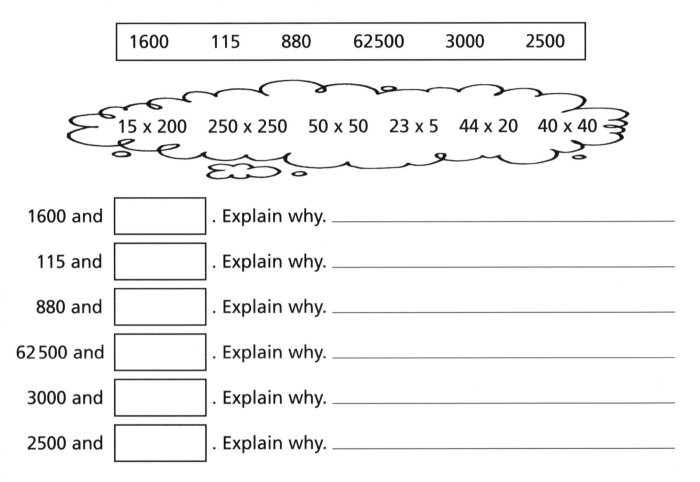

| 1600 | 115 | 880 | 62500 | 3000 | 2500 |

Bubble: 15 x 200   250 x 250   50 x 50   23 x 5   44 x 20   40 x 40

1600 and [   ] . Explain why. _____

115 and [   ] . Explain why. _____

880 and [   ] . Explain why. _____

62500 and [   ] . Explain why. _____

3000 and [   ] . Explain why. _____

2500 and [   ] . Explain why. _____

● The answer to each of the following calculations matches one of the statements. Estimate each answer and then draw lines to join each matching pair.

95000 – 94501	A number just under 1000.
6079 – 5078	A number just less than 100.
238 + 760	A number just less than 500.
12342 – 12241	A number just over 1000.
1356 – 855	A number just over 500.
1176 – 1077	A number just over 100.

Challenge

● Make up 5 of your own numbers and statements for a friend to match.

Understanding multiplication and division

Learning objectives

- ◆ Understand the idea of a remainder.
- ◆ Decide what to do after division and round up or down accordingly.

Resources

AS 'Remainders'

Teacher's notes

In this activity pupils use information on divisors and remainders to find unknown numbers. Go over the example given to ensure that pupils follow the reasoning.

1. A number, when divided by 5 and 3, leaves remainders of 1 and 1. Start with 5 + 1 = 6. Six is a multiple of 3. Go to 6 + 5 = 11. This leaves a remainder of 2 when divided by 3. Go to 11 + 5 = **16**. This is the answer.

2. A number, when divided by 6 and 7, leaves remainders of 0 and 4. The number must be a multiple of 6 since there is no remainder when it is divided by 6. Start with 6 + 6 = 12. This leaves a remainder of 5 when divided by 7. Go to **18**. This is the answer.

3. A number, when divided by 5 and 4, leaves remainders of 1 and 3. Start with 5 + 1 = 6 and then go to 6 + 5 = **11**. This is the answer.

4. A number, when divided by 3, 5 and 7, leaves remainders of 2, 3 and 2. Start with 7 + 2 = 9, then go to 9 + 7 = 16 and then to 16 + 7 = **23**. This is the answer. See if the pupils realise that (3 x 7) + 2 gives the answer. Hint: the answer has to be a multiple of 7 + 2.

5. A number, when divided by 2, 7 and 5, leaves remainders of 1, 1 and 0. The number must be a multiple of 5. It also equals 2 x 7 + 1 = **15**. This is the answer.

Remainders

Find a number using the clues about remainders.

Example:

> This number leaves a remainder of 3 when divided by 5 and a remainder of 1 when divided by 4.
>
> Start with 5 and add 3 so 5 + 3 = 8. This number leaves a remainder of 3 when divided by 5. But 8 leaves no remainder when divided by 4.
>
> Try adding another 5 to 8 so 5 + 8 = 13. This number leaves a remainder of 3 when divided by 5. It also leaves a remainder of 1 when divided by 4.
>
> The answer is 13.

● Find these numbers.

1. This number leaves remainders of 1 and 1 when divided by 5 and 3.

_____

2. This number leaves remainders of 0 and 4 when divided by 6 and 7.

_____

3. This number leaves remainders of 1 and 3 when divided by 5 and 4.

_____

4. This number leaves remainders of 2, 3 and 2 when divided by 3, 5 and 7.

_____

5. This number leaves remainders of 1,1 and 0 when divided by 2, 7 and 5.

_____

Challenge

● Make up a question on remainders for a friend to answer.

Making decisions and checking results

Learning objectives

- Choose and use appropriate number operations and appropriate ways of calculating to solve problems.
- Know and use the appropriate vocabulary.

Resources

AS 'How many?'

Teacher's notes

This activity is about sequences of numbers. Different arrangements of boxes are shown, and pupils have to work out the sequence and how it develops.

The first two arrangements of boxes are viewed from the side.

The first arrangement has layers of boxes developing from the top downwards in this sequence: 1 2 3 4. So 10 layers have 1 + 2 + 3 + ... + 10 boxes. Encourage the pupils to see the 10 layers as five pairs of numbers (1 + 10 , 2 + 9 , 3 + 8 , 4 + 7 , 6 + 5) that add up to 11. The total is 5 x 11 = **55**.

If there are 14 layers then there will be seven pairs of numbers, each adding up to 15. So, the total is 7 x 15 = 105. The 100th box must be in the **14th layer**.

In the second arrangement the boxes are double those in the first arrangement. In 10 layers there must be 2 x 55 = **110 boxes** (five pairs each adding up to 22 = 110).

The 200th box will be in the 14th layer. There are seven pairs of numbers, each adding up to 30. So, the total in 14 layers is 7 x 30 = 210. The 200th box is in **layer 14**.

The next set of boxes are viewed from above. Stack 1 has 1 box, stack 2 has 4 boxes, stack 3 has 10 and stack 4 has 20.
The stacks increase in the following way.

$$1 \rightarrow 4 \rightarrow 10 \rightarrow 20 \rightarrow 35 \rightarrow 56 \rightarrow 84 \rightarrow 120 \rightarrow 165 \rightarrow 220 \rightarrow 286 \rightarrow 364$$

Boxes added:	1	1	1	1	1						
	2	2	2	2	2						
		3	3	3	3						
			4	4	4						
				5	5						
					6						
Increase by:	3	6	10	15	21	28	36	45	55	66	78

Stack 6 has **56 boxes**.

Stack 12 has 364 boxes.

How many?

Here are some boxes stacked in layers.

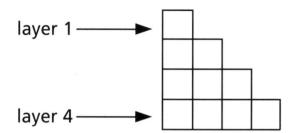

layer 1 ➝

layer 4 ➝

- How many boxes are in ten layers? _____

- In which layer is the 100th box? _____

Here is a different stack of boxes.

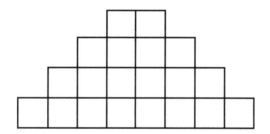

- How many boxes are in ten layers? _____

- In which layer is the 200th box? _____

Here are stacked boxes viewed from above.

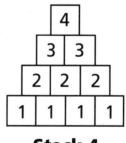

Stack 1   **Stack 2**   **Stack 3**   **Stack 4**

The numbers are the layers of boxes. In stack 3 there is a total of 10 boxes.

- How many boxes will there be in stack 6? _____

- Which stack will have 364 boxes? _____

Ratio and proportion

Learning objectives

- ◆ Solve simple problems involving ratio and proportion.
- ◆ Discuss statements relating to ratio and proportion facts.

Resources

AS 'Ratio sums'

Teacher's notes

This activity is about using ratio clues to solve problems. There are three parts.

1. The first question is about finding the different coins that add up to £4.50. First write down the given facts. (50p + 4 x 20p) + (5p + 5 x 2p) = (50p + 80p) + (5p + 10p) = £1.30 + 15p
Which combination(s) of £1.30 and 15p give a total of £4.50? Try some combinations. One £1.30 plus multiples of 15p cannot make a sum of £4.50. Neither can 2 x £1.30 plus multiples of 15p. But 3 x £1.30 plus 4 x 15p does equal £4.50.
The answer is **(3 x 50p) + (12 x 20p) + (4 x 5p) + (20 x 2p)** = £4.50.

2. The second question is about the relative sizes of four different masses. Write down the facts.
A = 3 x C; 2 x B = D; 2 x C = B; D = 4 x C.
Three statements are made about C: it has the smallest mass; D has the greatest mass; A has a greater mass than B.
Put the masses in order, starting with the heaviest: D A B C.
Start with a guess. Say C is 1kg. So B will be 2kg, A will be 3kg and D will be 4kg. This is one solution: **A = 3kg; B = 2kg; C = 1kg; D = 4kg**. Another solution is to double each mass:
A = 6kg; B = 4kg; C = 2kg; D = 8kg.

3. The last question is about working out the various ways in which a sum can be made from the three dice. The smallest sum is 3 (1 + 1 + 1); the largest sum is 9 (3 + 3 + 3).
The following combinations of 1, 2 and 3 make sums from 3 to 9:
One combination: 1 + 1 + 1 makes 3.
Three combinations: 1 + 1 + 2, 1 + 2 + 1, 2 + 1 + 1 make 4.
Six combinations: 1 + 2 + 2, 2 + 1 + 2, 2 + 2 + 1, 1 + 3 + 1, 1 + 1 + 3, 3 + 1 + 1 make 5.
Seven combinations: 1 + 2 + 3, 1 + 3 + 2, 3 + 1 + 2, 3 + 2 + 1, 2 + 3 + 1, 2 + 1 + 3, 2 + 2 + 2 make 6.
Six combinations: 1 + 3 + 3, 3 + 1 + 3, 3 + 3 + 1, 2 + 2 + 3, 2 + 3 + 2, 3 + 2 + 2 make 7.
Three combinations: 2 + 3 + 3, 3 + 3 + 2, 3 + 2 + 3 make 8.
One combination: 3 + 3 + 3 makes 9.

Notice the symmetry of the combinations: 1, 3, 6, 7, 6, 3, 1 (a total of 3 x 3 x 3 = 27).

Yes, Natasha is correct. There are six ways to score 7 and three ways to score 4.
No, Tim is wrong. There are seven ways to score 7 and one way to score 9.

Ratio sums

1. You have a total of £4.50. For every 50p coin you have four 20p coins and for every 5p coin you have five 2p coins.

- What coins do you have? _____

_____

2. Work out the masses A, B, C and D in kilograms. Each mass is a whole number and is less than 10kg. There are two possible solutions.

One of A is as heavy as three of C.   Two of B are as heavy as one of D.

Two of C are as heavy as one of B.   One of D is as heavy as four of C.

_____

_____

3. This is a triangular dice that has the numbers 1, 2, 3 on three of its sides.

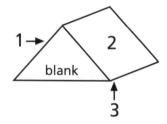

The two ends are blank.

Natasha and Tim are throwing three of these dice together and adding up their scores. Natasha says that there are twice as many ways to score 7 than to score 4.

Is she correct? Circle your answer. **Yes/No**

- Explain your answer. _____

_____

Tim adds that there are five times as many ways to score 6 than to score 9.

Is he correct? Circle your answer. **Yes/No**

- Explain your answer. _____

_____

Fractions, decimals and percentages

Learning objectives

- ◆ Recognise the equivalence between percentages, fractions and decimals.
- ◆ Find simple percentages of numbers.

Resources

AS 'Missing numbers'

Teacher's notes

The equations in this activity have numbers in both fraction and decimal form. Consequently, to find the missing numbers pupils have to know the equivalent values of different fractions and decimals.

1. Since $0.5 + 0.25 = 0.75$ then the missing number is $1 - 0.75 = 0.25$ or $\frac{1}{4}$.

2. Since $\frac{3}{4} = 0.75$ then $0.75 + \frac{3}{4} = 1.5$. The missing number is $2 - 1.5 = \textbf{0.5}$.

3. Convert $\frac{4}{5}$ to $\frac{8}{10}$ so $\frac{8}{10} + \frac{1}{10} = \frac{9}{10}$ or 0.9. The missing number is $1 - 0.9 = \textbf{0.1}$.

4. Since $\frac{1}{4} = 0.25$ then $\frac{1}{4} + 1.25 = 1\frac{1}{2}$. The missing number is $2 - 1\frac{1}{2} = \frac{1}{2}$.

5. Since $\frac{5}{2} = 2.5$ then $1.5 + 2.5 + 2.2 = 6.2$. The missing number is $7 - 6.2 = 0.8$ or $\frac{4}{5}$.

6. Since $2.7 - 0.3 = 2.4$ the missing number is $2.4 - 1.5 = 0.9$ or $\frac{9}{10}$.

7. Convert $\frac{1}{5}$ to 0.2 so $10 - 8.2 - 0.2 = \textbf{1.6}$.

8. Convert $\frac{1}{4}$ to 0.25 so $2.75 - 2.5 + 0.25 = 0.5$ or $\frac{1}{2}$.

Two possible solutions to the last number sentence are:
$10 - \frac{7}{2} = 5 + \textbf{1.5}$ and
$10 - \frac{22}{10} = 5 + \textbf{2.8}$

Missing numbers

● These number sentences have numbers in both decimal and fraction forms. One number is missing from each number sentence. Find this number and write it in the empty box.

1. [ ] + 0.50 + 0.25 = 1 Write the missing number as a fraction.

2. 0.75 + $\frac{3}{4}$ + [ ] = 2 Write the missing number as a decimal.

3. $\frac{4}{5}$ + $\frac{1}{10}$ + [ ] = 1 Write the missing number as a decimal.

4. $\frac{1}{4}$ + [ ] + 1.25 = 2 Write the missing number as a fraction.

5. 1.5 + $\frac{5}{2}$ + 2.2 + [ ] = 7 Write the missing number as a fraction.

6. 2.7 – 0.3 – [ ] = 1.5 Write the missing number as a fraction.

7. 10 – 8.2 – $\frac{1}{5}$ = [ ] Write the missing number as a decimal.

8. 2.75 – 2.5 + $\frac{1}{4}$ = [ ] Write the missing number as a fraction.

● Find two solutions for this number sentence. Write the number on the left side as a fraction and the number on the right side as a decimal.

10 – [ ] = 5 + [ ]

10 – [ ] = 5 + [ ]

Handling data

Learning objectives

◆ Make a prediction based on a set of data.
◆ Collect a set of data.
◆ Organise results.

Resources

AS 'Combinations'

Teacher's notes

This activity is about the different ways in which three numbers can be selected from six. With the card game there are 20 possible combinations of three numbers selected from six. These are presented below, with the total for each set of three numbers:

Totals:	6	7	8	9	10	11	12	13	14	15
	1+2+3	1+2+4	1+2+5	1+2+6						
			1+3+4	1+3+5	1+3+6					
				1+4+5	1+4+6					
						1+5+6				
				2+3+4	2+3+5	2+3+6				
						2+4+5	2+4+6			
							2+5+6			
						3+4+5	3+4+6	3+5+6		
									4+5+6	
	1	1	2	3	3	3	3	2	1	1

The range of totals is 6 to 15 with 9, 10, 11 and 12 appearing three times each.

When pupils carry out this analysis of the combinations encourage them to be systematic in their approach. It is very easy to miss out some combinations if the analysis is done in a haphazard way.

Theresa is wrong. When a dice is thrown three times there is a possibility of throwing the same number each time. This does not happen with the cards since each of the three cards is picked up. So there are fewer cards left to choose from when the second and third cards are selected. The card game would be the same as throwing the dice if the following method was used. Lift a card up, check the number, return the card to be mixed in with the other five cards, lift up a second card. Do this three times.

There are 6 x 6 x 6 = 216 possible combinations of numbers from three throws of a dice.

Combinations

Theresa and Carl are playing a game with six numbered cards.

1	2	3	4	5	6

The cards are face down so the numbers cannot be seen.
One player picks up three cards and adds the numbers. The cards are put down and mixed up. Then the next player picks up three cards. Whoever gets the highest total wins. After playing this game for a while Carl notices that some totals seem to appear more often than others.

● Which totals do you think will appear most often? Explain your reasoning.

_____

_____

_____

_____

Theresa suggests that instead of picking up three cards they could throw a dice three times and add the numbers. She explains that because a dice is numbered one to six it will be exactly the same as picking up three cards.

● Is she correct? Circle your answer. **Yes/No**

● Will the range of possible totals be the same? Explain your answer.

_____

_____

_____

_____

 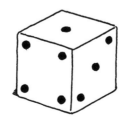 

Using a calculator

Learning objectives

- ◆ Use a calculator efficiently.
- ◆ Check answers of calculations.
- ◆ Use decimals and decimal points confidently on a calculator.

Resources

AS 'Multipliers'
Calculators

Teacher's notes

In this activity pupils have to estimate products and then compare the values. Although the calculations are to be carried out mentally, allow pupils to jot down estimations and ideas. They should not however, carry out the full multiplication.

1. **12 x 10.5** = 126 is the largest product. 10.5 x 12 = (10 x 12) + (0.5 x 12) and is greater than 12.5 x 10 = (12 x 10) + (0.5 x 10) = 125.

2. 25 x 36 = 36 x 100/4 = 9 x 100 = 900 and **21 x 45** = (20 x 45) + 45 = 900 + 45 = 945.

3. 45 is half of 90 but 31 is more than 2 x 15. So **45 x 31** must be greater than 90 x 15.

4. 4.1 x 20 = (4 x 20) + (0.1 x 20) whereas 4.0 x 21 = (4 x 20) + (4 x 1). So **21 x 4.0** is greater.

The next set of calculations involve additions and subtractions as well as multiplications.

5. Since 15 x 101 = (15 x 100) + 15 = (1.5 x 1000) + 15, then **1.5 x 1000 + 10** must produce the smaller number.

6. Since 76 x 99 = (76 x 100) – 76, then **76 x 100 – 100** must produce the smaller number.

7. Since 23 x 999.9 = (23 x 1000) – (23 x 0.1) and (22 x 1000) + 999 = 23 x (1000 – 1) then **23 x 999.9** must produce the smaller number.

8. Since 19.5 x 50 = (19 x 50) + (0.5 x 50) and 50.5 x 19 = (50 x 19) + (0.5 x 19) then the smaller product must be **50.5 x 19**.

9. 20 x 25 = 500 and 20 x 25 x 9.9 = 500 x (10 – 0.1) = 5000 – 50 = **4950**.

10. 40 x 50 = 2000 and 2000 x 10.1 = 20000 + 200 = **20200**.

Multipliers

● Each pair of products are similar in value. Estimate each answer mentally. Underline the one that you think will produce the **greater** number. Then check your answer using a calculator and circle **Yes** or **No**.

1. 10 x 12.5   12 x 10.5   Were you correct? **Yes/No**

2. 25 x 36   21 x 45   Were you correct? **Yes/No**

3. 90 x 15   45 x 31   Were you correct? **Yes/No**

4. 4.1 x 20   21 x 4.0   Were you correct? **Yes/No**

● The answers to each of these pairs of calculations are similar in value. Estimate each answer mentally. Underline the one that you think will produce the **smaller** number. Then check your answer using a calculator and circle **Yes** or **No**.

5. 15 x 101   1.5 x 1000 + 10   Were you correct? **Yes/No**

6. 76 x 99   76 x 100 – 100   Were you correct? **Yes/No**

7. 23 x 999.9   22 x 1000 + 999   Were you correct? **Yes/No**

8. 19.5 x 50   50.5 x 19   Were you correct? **Yes/No**

● Estimate the answers to these two calculations. Write each answer as a whole number.

9. 20 x 25 x 9.9 = _____

10. 40 x 50 x 10.1 = _____

Shape, space and measures

Learning objectives

◆ Use a protractor to measure angles.
◆ Recognise 'acute', 'right' and 'obtuse' angles.
◆ Draw angles with a protractor.

Resources

AS 'Polygons'
Protractors, rulers and plain card

Teacher's notes

In this activity paper or card is cut into triangle shapes which are then used to construct different polygons.

The simplest shape to make is a square.

A right-angled triangle moved round the centre creates a square.

Next is a pentagon.

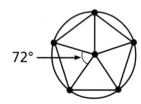

An isosceles triangle, with an angle of 72°, moved round the centre creates a pentagon.

Ask pupils how they might make these two shapes using one triangle for each.

Emphasise the need for care and patience when drawing the polygons. A dot that is slightly out of place can easily lead to a distorted shape.

After pupils have practised making polygons, talk to them about the kinds of designs they can make using these methods. A smaller or larger triangle can be used to make different sizes of polygons. Here are some design ideas.

Two hexagons are rotated about the same centre.

A series of pentagons are translated.

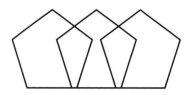

One polygon can be drawn inside another polygon.

Polygons

- Follow these instructions to draw a **hexagon** on a sheet of paper.

    Step 1: Make an equilateral triangle from card. Make each side 5cm long.

    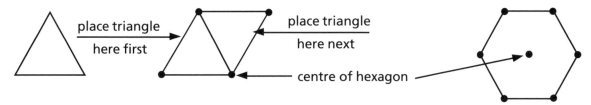

    Step 2: Place the triangle on a sheet of paper with one side horizontal. On the paper, mark a dot at each corner.
    Step 3: Join the two outer dots by a straight line. The third dot is the centre.
    Step 4: Move the triangle round the centre. At each new position join the outer dots. A hexagon is created.

- Follow these instructions to draw a **heptagon** on a sheet of paper.

    Step 1: Make an isosceles triangle from card. Make the sides 5cm, 4cm and 4cm long.

    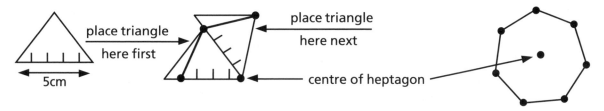

    Step 2: Place the triangle on a sheet of paper with the 5cm side horizontal. On the paper, mark one dot 4cm along the 5cm side and another dot at the corner.
    Step 3: Join the two outer dots by a straight line. The third dot is the centre.
    Step 4: Move the triangle round the centre. At each new position join the outer dots. A heptagon is created.

- Follow these instructions to draw a nine-sided polygon, called a **nonagon**, on a sheet of paper.

    Step 1: Make a right-angled triangle from card. Make the sides 3cm, 4cm and 5cm long.

    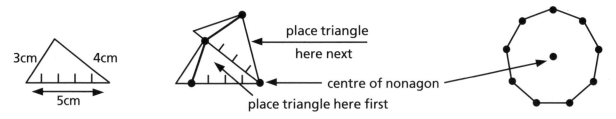

    Step 2: Place the triangle on a sheet of paper with the 5cm side horizontal. Mark one dot 4cm along the 5cm side and another dot at the corner. The third dot is in the centre.
    Step 3: Move the triangle round the centre. At each new position join the outer dots. A nonagon is created.

Use these methods and your teacher's ideas to create your own designs.

Shape, space and measures

Learning objectives

- ◆ Recognise parallel lines.
- ◆ Recognise perpendicular lines.
- ◆ Draw parallel and perpendicular lines accurately.
- ◆ Select correct tools to work with.
- ◆ Draw lines to 1mm.

Resources

AS 'Curves'
Rulers, protractors, compasses and sharp pencils

Teacher's notes

In this activity pupils are shown how to make two curved shapes from straight lines. They are the astroid (star shape) and the cardioid (heart shape). Ensure that pupils understand the instructions for making these shapes. Using a sharp pencil leads to the best results.

The length of each line can be greater or less than 5cm. This length was only chosen to create an astroid of reasonable size. The astroid is easy to draw and the results are pleasing. Different coloured pens or pencils can be used to create different effects.

The cardioid takes a little longer to construct because the circle has to be numbered fairly accurately. Pupils should use a protractor to mark out 10° divisions. Once pupils have joined 18 to 36 then they have been once around the circle. Since 2 x 19 = 38 (36 + 2), join 19 to 2. Carefully go over the envelope of lines with a dark pen or pencil to emphasise the heart shape.

A shape called a nephroid (kidney shape) is created in a circle when different pairs of numbers are joined by straight lines. These number pairs are 1 to 3, 2 to 6, 3 to 9, 4 to 12 ... 12 to 36 ... 20 to 60 (36 + 24) ... up to 35 to 105 (105 = [2 x 36] + 33).

A nephroid (kidney shape)

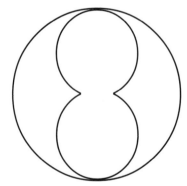

When creating their designs pupils could be encouraged to make different sized astroids using various colours. They might also like to incorporate circles and squares into their designs.

Curves

- Practise drawing these two curves that can be created by drawing straight lines.

The astroid
(star shape)

5cm straight
lines

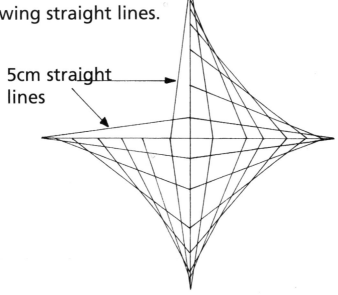

Step 1: Draw two perpendicular lines or axes to make four quadrants.
Step 2: In each quadrant draw a series of 5cm lines to join the horizontal axis to the vertical axis.

The cardioid
(heart shape)

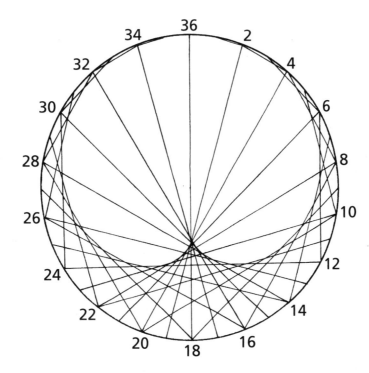

Step 1: Draw a circle and number it (only even numbers are shown).
Step 2: Join 1 to 2, 2 to 4, 3 to 6 ... 18 to 36, 19 to 38 (36 + 2) ... up to 35 to 70 (36 + 34).

- Create another design that uses these curves. Your teacher has some ideas to help you with the design.

Shape, space and measures

Learning objectives

- ◆ Use understanding of measurement and units within a context.
- ◆ Interpret a question.
- ◆ Check results of calculations by appropriate strategies.

Resources

AS 'Frames'

Teacher's notes

In this problem-solving activity pupils have to work out the lengths of wood strip to make photograph frames.

1. There are three square frames with sides of 30cm, 20cm and 10cm.
   The length needed is (4 x 30cm) + (4 x 20cm) + (4 x 10cm) = 120cm + 80cm + 40cm = **240cm**.

2. There are four 1m, or 4 x 100cm, lengths of wood strip. Two kinds of square frame are being made, with sides of 15cm and 35cm. Ask the children why only one side needs to be specified for a square.

   The wood strip can be cut the following way.

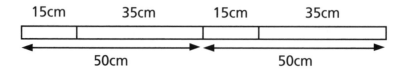

| 15cm | 35cm | 15cm | 35cm |

← 50cm → ← 50cm →

   Since 15cm + 35cm = 50cm, two pieces of each can be cut from 1m length of wood strip. From four x 1m lengths of wood strip it is possible to cut eight pieces each of 15cm and 35cm. Each frame requires four pieces. So **two square frames with sides of 15cm and two with sides of 35cm can be made**.

3. The third problem is more easily visualised and solved using a diagram.

16cm 16cm 16cm 16cm 16cm 16cm	6 x 16cm = 96cm. 4cm is left.
24cm 24cm 24cm 24cm	4 x 24cm = 96cm. 4cm is left.
24cm 24cm 24cm 24cm	4 x 24cm = 96cm. 4cm is left.
24cm 24cm 16cm 16cm 16cm	2 x 24cm + 3 x 16cm = 96cm. 4cm is left.
24cm 24cm 16cm 16cm 16cm	2 x 24cm + 3 x 16cm = 96cm. 4cm is left.

   Twelve pieces each of 24cm and 16cm can be cut. **Six frames can be made**, and there is 5 x 4cm = **20cm of wood strip left**.

Frames

1. Senem and Jade are making some wooden
frames for their family photographs. Each frame
is to be made from four lengths of wood strip
that are glued together to form a square.

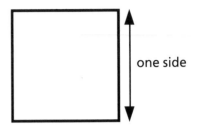

one side

- What total length of wood strip do they need for
  three square frames with sides of 30cm, 20cm and 10cm? _____

- Explain how you worked out the length.

_____

_____

_____

2. Michelle and Ian have four 1m lengths of wood strip. They are making two
kinds of square frame, with sides of 15cm and 35cm. They want the same
number of each kind of frame.

- How many of each can they make from their wood strip? _____

- Explain your answer.

_____

_____

_____

3. Hannah wants as many rectangular frames, measuring 24cm x 16cm, as
possible from five x 1m lengths of wood strip.

- How many frames can she make and will any wood strip be left?

_____

- Explain your answers.

_____

_____

_____

_____

Mental calculation strategies for addition and subtraction

Learning objectives

◆ Use known number facts and place value to add or subtract a pair of numbers mentally.

Resources

AS 'Multiples of 9'

Teacher's notes

This activity is in the form of an investigation into the subtraction of pairs of numbers.

Two digits separated by 1 are combined to make two numbers. Then the two numbers are subtracted. The difference is always 9. For example, 1 and 2 make 12 and 21. Subtracting, 21 – 12 = 9. This is easily explained. Of the two-digit numbers made, the larger number has a tens digit 1 more than the smaller number (10 units more). The smaller number has a units digit 1 more than the larger number (1 unit more). The difference between the two numbers is always 10 – 1 = 9.

When the two digits are separated by 2, similar reasoning applies. The larger number is greater by 2 tens units (20). The smaller number has a units digit that is 2 greater than that of the larger number. The difference between the two numbers is 20 – 2 = 18 or 2 x 9.

This reasoning applies to digits up to 1 and 9, where 91 – 19 = 72 or (8 x 9). All the pairs of numbers differ by multiples of 9.

Using 0 produces some interesting results. With 0 and 1, 10 – 01 = 10 – 1 = 9. With 0 and 9, 90 – 09 = 90 – 9 = 81 or (9 x 9).

Adding an extra digit to form a three-digit number increases the result, but the difference is still a multiple of 9. For example, putting a 5 between 87 and 78 makes 857 and 758. Subtracting 857 – 758 = 99.

Explanation
The hundreds digits for the larger number is 1 greater than for the smaller number, so the numbers differ by 100. The tens digits are the same. The units digit for the smaller number is 1 greater than that for the larger number. The two numbers therefore differ by 100 – 1 = 99. Thus, reversing the digits of any three-digit number and subtracting the two numbers will result in a third number that is always a multiple of 9.

In fact, the difference of any number and its reverse is always a multiple of 9.
For example, 43 201 – 10 234 = 32 967 or (9 x 3663).
This is explained by partitioning the numbers:
43 201 = 40 001 + (320 x 10) and 10 234 = 10 004 + (23 x 10).

Thus, 43 201 – 10 234 = (40 001 – 10 004) + 10 x (320 – 023).
The answers to both the calculations in brackets are multiples of 9. Therefore, the two five-digit numbers differ by a multiple of 9.

Multiples of 9

1. Take two digits that are separated by 1.
Make two numbers from the digits. Subtract
the smaller number from the larger number.
Try this with other pairs of digits that differ by 1.

For example, 7 and 8.
78 and 87.
87 – 78 = 9.

- What did you find? _____

- Can you explain this? _____

_____

_____

2. Do the same with two digits that are separated by 2.
Make two numbers from the digits.
Subtract the smaller from the larger number.
Try this with other pairs of digits that differ by 2.

For example, 3 and 5.
35 and 53.
53 – 35 = 18.

- What did you find? _____

- Can you explain this? _____

_____

_____

3. Try this with other pairs of digits that differ by 3, 4, 5 and 6.

- What did you find? _____

- Can you explain this? _____

_____

_____

4. Put an extra digit between some of your pairs of digits.
For example, what happens if the numbers are 857 and 758 or 523
and 325?

_____

_____

_____

Properties of numbers

Learning objectives

◆ Investigate number sequences.

Resources

AS 'Magic squares'

Teacher's notes

In this activity pupils investigate a statement about number sequences and magic squares.

The numbers 1 to 9 fit into a magic square.

8	1	6
3	5	7
4	9	2

The magic number of a magic square is always
3 x the centre number.
In this square the magic number is 3 x 5 = **15**.

Once the first square has been completed it can be used to help fit in other number sequences.
Just follow the same pattern. Put the smallest number in the 1 position and continue until the
largest number is put in the 9 position.

In the second sequence, each number is
separated by 3.

24	3	18
9	15	21
12	27	6

The magic number is 3 x 15 = **45**.

With a regular number sequence, the central number, such as 5 and 15, is in the middle square.
Pairs of numbers that are on either side of this central number in a sequence are also opposite
each other in the magic square.
For example, look at the sequence 1, 2, 3, 4, 5, 6, 7, 8, 9. The number pairs 1, 9; 2, 8; 3, 7 and 4,
6 are opposite each other in the magic square. Each of these number pairs have sums of 10, so
when they are added to 5 the total is 15, which is the magic number.

Notice that the diagonals also follow sequences.
2, 5, 8 and 4, 5, 6 for the first square.
6, 15, 24 and 12, 15, 18 for the second square.

The central rows and columns also follow sequences.
1, 5, 9 and 3, 5, 7 for the first square.
3, 15, 27 and 9, 15, 21 for the second square.

Magic squares

Any regular sequence of nine numbers can be made into a magic square.

● Test this statement by putting some numbers into the 3 x 3 square. The square must be magic, which means that the three numbers in each side and in both diagonals must add up to the same total, called the magic number.

Use the numbers: 1, 2, 3, 4, 5, 6, 7, 8, 9.

What is the magic number? _____

● Try this with another number sequence:

3, 6, 9, 12, 15, 18, 21, 24, 27.

What is the magic number? _____

● Write a number sequence of your own and fit the numbers in a magic square.

My number sequence is

_____

The magic number is _____ .

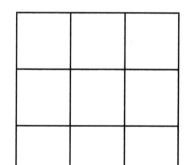

● In these magic squares can you see anything interesting about the numbers in the diagonals and rows?

_____

_____

United Kingdom: Folens Publishers, Apex Business Centre, Boscombe Road, Dunstable, LU5 4RL.
Email: folens@folens.com

Ireland: Folens Publishers, Greenhills Road, Tallaght, Dublin 24.
Email: info@folens.ie

Poland: JUKA, ul. Renesansowa 38, Warsaw 01-905

Editor: Katherine Seddon
Layout artist: Patricia Hollingsworth
Illustrations: Kirsty Wilson of Graham-Cameron Illustration
Cover design: Martin Cross

First published 2001 by Folens Limited.
Reprinted 2002.

British Library Cataloguing in Publication Data. A catalogue record for this book is available from the British Library.

ISBN 1 84163 940–0